TID-26373

# AN ATLAS OF
# RF MOUSE PATHOLOGY:
## DISEASE DESCRIPTIONS AND INCIDENCES

N. K. Clapp

Biology Division
Oak Ridge National Laboratory

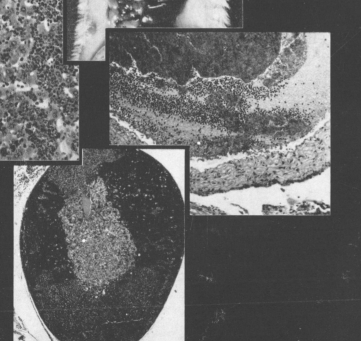

Technical Information Center, Office of Information Services
UNITED STATES ATOMIC ENERGY COMMISSION

**About the Cover.** This design demonstrates myeloid leukemia with a number of its unique histological manifestations; this disease is radiogenic in RF mice and has served as an experimental model to further our understanding of leukemias.

Available as TID-26373 for $5.45 ($7.95 foreign) from

National Technical Information Service
U. S. Department of Commerce
Springfield, Virginia 22151

Library of Congress Catalog Card Number 73-600220
AEC Distribution Category UC-48

Printed in the United States of America
USAEC Technical Information Center, Oak Ridge, Tennessee

September 1973; latest printing, April 1974

TID-26373

# AN ATLAS OF

# RF MOUSE PATHOLOGY:

## DISEASE DESCRIPTIONS AND INCIDENCES

N. K. Clapp

Biology Division
Oak Ridge National Laboratory

September 1973

Research sponsored by the U. S. Atomic Energy Commission under contract with Union Carbide Corporation

Published by

Technical Information Center, Office of Information Services
UNITED STATES ATOMIC ENERGY COMMISSION

6-13-74

**ACKNOWLEDGEMENT**. The author is indebted to William D. Gude and his staff for the preparation of the histological material and to the Editorial Staff of the Biology Division for invaluable assistance in preparing the manuscript and photographs.

# Contents

# Introduction

Complete necropsy data for most inbred strains of mice is rarely found in the literature. Either the data are abundant on a particular organ or system of interest [e.g., reticular neoplasms (1)] or the extent of examination is inconsistent from mouse-to-mouse, ranging from only mortality data on one animal to complete histologic examination of all organs on another. The parameters needed by the investigator for determining experimental design are often lacking, as became apparent during a large experiment (3135 mice of the RF strain) to determine relative biological effectiveness (RBE) of 60-MeV protons and 300-kVp X rays [see ref. 18]. While much information had been gathered regarding numerous organ and system responses of the RF mouse to radiation (2-15), we had difficulty in making comparisons with previous studies because of the inconsistencies in methodology of observation from study to study. Therefore, during our experiment, we collected and recorded pathological data on the 526 control mice as completely as for the irradiated mice, in order to establish baseline pathology data for female mice of this strain. The baseline pathology data is reported here primarily for use in future experiments with RF mice; irradiation procedures and the detailed experimental results on the irradiated mice, utilizing the baseline data for comparison, are reported elsewhere (17, 18).

---

# Materials and Methods

## ANIMAL SELECTION, CARE, AND OBSERVATION

All mice entered this experiment as young-adult (8-week-old) virgin females from a noninbred stock derived from the RF/Un strain. They were selected from a colony established in the Biology Division of the Oak Ridge National Laboratory by Dr. Jacob Furth and in later years maintained by Dr. Arthur C. Upton and coworkers. The mice were housed in nonbarrier conditions with high standards of hygiene and husbandry. Only the responsible caretaker and those persons involved in the experiment were allowed in contact with the mice at any time. Temperature and relative humidity were monitored and closely regulated.

Mice had free access to Purina Laboratory Chow and to water from bottles that were changed twice weekly. Cages were cleaned and sterilized twice weekly and new wood shavings were placed therein. Mice were removed from the room only for irradiation or sham exposure. They were then returned to live out their life-spans, except that some mice were removed periodically for slit-lamp examination of the lens (16). All cages were checked twice daily, and moribund animals were killed and tissues taken for histologic examination. All mice were necropsied as soon after death as possible.

## NECROPSY PROCEDURE

Each mouse was first examined for external lesions; then it was laid on its back and pinned to a paraffin block. A midline incision through the skin was made from the anus to the mandibular symphysis and the skin was reflected to reveal the superficial lymph nodes and other subcutaneous tissues. A deeper midline incision opened the thorax and abdomen (Fig. 1). Each organ of the major systems of the body was examined systematically. After the thoracic and abdominal viscera were examined, the cranium was opened and its contents, including the pituitary gland, were observed. Tissues routinely taken for microscopic examination were: superficial and deep lymph nodes

Necropsy Record Card (reverse)

(~50% reduction)

Necropsy Record Card (face)

History of animal, gross necropsy observations, histological information, and tissues observed both grossly and histologically were recorded on this card.
Data were then transcribed, coded, and entered into computer storage.

(including the mesenteric lymph node), sternum, lungs, thymus, heart, liver, kidneys, stomach, small intestine, ovaries, uterus, urinary bladder, spleen, pancreas, brain, and pituitary gland. About 80% of the mice were examined histologically. Tissues were preserved in Zenker-formol fixative, embedded in paraffin, and stained routinely with hematoxylin and eosin. Special stains were employed where indicated.

Gross and histologic pathology information and the historical data were recorded in detail and stored on specially designed necropsy record cards. Pathological information was then coded and entered into a computer (Call-A-Computer, Raleigh, North Carolina) for storage and further statistical analysis. Special emphasis was placed upon the following diseases: thymic lymphoma, myeloid leukemia, reticulum cell sarcoma, nonthymic lymphoma, lung and ovarian tumors, glomerulosclerosis and uterine hyperplasia. Other less frequently occurring diseases are described in lesser detail.

# Results

## PATHOLOGY

### Neoplastic Diseases

#### Leukemias and Leukemoid Reaction

**Thymic lymphoma: Gross appearance.** — This early-occurring lymphoma [mean survival time (MST) of affected mice = 455 days] developed in the thymus and involved primarily the mediastinal organs, with subsequent metastatic involvement of other organs and systems. The animal usually exhibited dyspnea and hyperpnea. Sudden death followed, often occurring when the mouse was handled. Cyanosis was common. At necropsy, a large, firm, white mediastinal mass occupied the entire anterior portion of the thoracic cavity, displacing the heart and lungs posteriorly (Fig. 2). The thymus engulfed the heart (Fig. 3) and conformed to the pressures and confinement imposed by the rib cage. A white material of cheesy consistency was often seen on the pericardium and pleura; the lungs were most often atelectatic. In a fulminating case, the organs of the thoracic cavity may be the only ones involved. In more slowly developing lymphomas, the leukemic cells may spread to almost all the tissues of the body, principally via the blood stream. The liver, spleen, ovaries, uterus and peripheral lymph nodes were frequent sites of involvement when the lymphoma became generalized (Fig. 4). The spleen and liver were usually smooth on the surface and moderately enlarged; the liver was either dark chocolate in color or pale, as the ovaries and kidneys usually were. For evaluation purposes, we have described these lymphomas by the degree of involvement as thymic only (restricted to the thoracic cavity) or thymic with generalized involvement.

**Thymic lymphoma: Histopathology.** — Architecture of the thymus was destroyed and a homogenous mass of leukemic cells was seen (Fig. 5). The leukemic cells infiltrated the base of the heart (Fig. 6), invaded the pericardium (Fig. 7), and followed the bronchial and vascular tree in the lungs as they presented a "cuffing" around most pulmonary arteries and larger air passageways (Fig. 8). The lymphoma invaded the liver perivascularly, with the primary initial concentration in the portal triads; it was often associated with a fatty infiltration within the liver parenchyma, which exhibited a pale yellow color on gross observation (Fig. 9). Infiltration of the spleen occurred initially in the red pulp (Fig. 10), and could become so extensive that splenic architecture was no longer recognizable (Fig. 11). The kidney was also frequently infiltrated (Fig. 12), as were the ovary, uterus (Fig. 13), and lymph nodes throughout the body (Fig. 14). The ovaries were usually infiltrated to the same degree bilaterally, and care was necessary to avoid a false diagnosis of bilaterial ovarian tumor. The cell type was very consistent: uniform in size, with peripheral accumulation of nuclear chromatin, scanty cytoplasm, prominent nucleolus, and a general resemblance to an immature lymphocyte (Fig. 15). The leukemic cell appeared morphologically the same regardless of organ distribution, with only the course of the disease affecting the degree of organ involvement.

**Myeloid leukemia: Gross appearance.** — The granulocytic form of leukemia in RF mice (MST=622 days) routinely involved the spleen and liver as the primary organs and was manifest as marked hepatomegaly and splenomegaly (Fig. 16). The organs were usually very smooth, in contrast to the nodular appearance of reticulum cell sarcoma, and of a brownish color with a greenish hue in some cases. The latter has been designated a chloromyeloid leukemia. The spleen and liver may reach three to five times their normal size. A generalized icterus and anemia were common observations. Lymph nodes were often secondarily involved and reached five to ten times normal size, with primarily leukemic and some inflammatory cell infiltration. Two other frequent gross observations accompanying myeloid leukemia were petechiae in the lungs (Fig. 16) and selective necrosis of some compartments of the sternal bone marrow, leaving a pale compartment which contrasted with the darker cell-filled compartments of both normal and leukemic mice.

**Myeloid leukemia: Histopathology.** — Myeloid leukemia appeared to develop in the red pulp of the spleen and usually overwhelmed the remaining normal components, eventually destroying the architecture (Figs 17, 18). Although the dominant cells within the leukemic spleen were of granulocytic origin, megakaryocytopoiesis and erythropoiesis were sometimes evident, and remnants of the white pulp components were visible (Fig. 19). Potentially, any stage of granulocytic maturation may become leukemic, but the most frequent cell type was identified as a metamyelocyte, the morphology consisting of an indented nucleus (Fig. 20). Other forms were seen, and included some which would be considered as undifferentiated stem cell types. Mature forms were occasionally seen. In the liver the preponderant infiltration was perivascular about the central veins and portal triads, but the sinusoids were usually markedly distended with leukemic cells; the cellular distribution was more diffuse throughout the entire liver than the pattern seen in thymic lymphomas (Figs 21, 22; cf. Fig. 9). Another organ frequently infiltrated with leukemic cells was the adrenal cortex (Figs 23, 24). Figures 25 and 26 show normal cellular components of the spleen and megakaryocytosis and erythropoiesis in the red pulp, with an abundance of myeloid leukemia cells invading it. Most often, myeloid leukemia cells invaded the blood stream, and extremely high white blood cell counts were observed (Fig. 27). Emboli of leukemic cells were common findings in the lungs (Fig. 28) and heart. Thromboses often resulted, and petechial hemorrhages were associated with the blockage of the smaller pulmonary arteries (Fig. 29). Necrosis of bone marrow cells was almost complete in one or more compartments of the sternum, while other compartments remained full of leukemic cells (Fig. 30). The etiology of this condition is uncertain, but may relate to leukemic emboli causing an interruption in blood supply as was observed in the lungs.

**Reticulum cell sarcoma: Gross appearance.** — Various sites and degrees of involvement were seen with this widely variant and late-occurring leukemia (MST=659 days). The generalized reticulum cell sarcoma most often involved the spleen, liver, and lymph nodes (Fig. 31), although any or nearly all organs may contain primary as well as metastatic foci. The spleen and liver were light brown in color and very nodular; cut sections confirmed the nodularity, which is white and firm (Fig. 32). In the spleen, the lymphatic nodule was primarily involved at from one to many sites. The peripheral lymph nodes were usually markedly enlarged, reaching five to ten times normal size. The thymus may be involved secondarily. Single organs, such as the mesenteric lymph node and spleen, may be involved, especially early in the course of the disease.

**Reticulum cell sarcoma: Histopathology.** — Proliferation of reticulum cells began in the white pulp of the spleen

and, through pressure, caused alteration of the architecture such as might result from inflation of a balloon in a confined area (Fig. 33). Hemopoietic activity of the red pulp continued despite the pressure exerted and the altered architecture. Several cellular variants of this leukemia were seen, although a single cell type was usually dominant in each case. The cells were usually pleomorphic, although they retained their reticular nature intranuclearly. The predominant leukemic cells may range from those with small nuclei with an abundant eosinophilic cytoplasm to those of more typical reticular form with large pale nuclei with prominent nucleoli and abundant cytoplasm (Figs 34–36). Some resembled a fibrosarcoma with whorl patterns, especially in the uterus. We have not seen any correlation of cell type with specific sites of involvement. In the liver, leukemic cells tended to group together in relatively well-circumscribed nodular formation, resulting in localized massive obliteration and displacement of the liver parenchyma (Figs 37, 38).

Reticulum cell sarcoma restricted to the abdominal cavity frequently involved the mesenteric lymph node as an apparent site of origin (Figs 39, 40), although other abdominal lymph nodes, Peyer's patches (Fig. 41), liver (Fig. 42), and spleen may be involved, alone or with other organs. As in the generalized distribution, there was no evidence of correlation between cell type and distribution of the leukemic involvement. The thymus was involved secondarily on occasion (Fig. 43), but the leukemic cells were reticular and not lymphomatous (Fig. 44). The bone marrow was rarely involved. One variant which was occasionally seen included giant cells with peripheral nuclei, and had some resemblance to the human Hodgkin's disease (Fig. 45). In RF mice, we have not yet identified a syndrome exactly analogous to Hodgkin's disease. Involvement of the blood stream was not usual in the majority of cases, but occasionally leukemic cells were seen intravascularly in large numbers.

**Nonthymic lymphoma.** — A number of late-occurring leukemias which were described as lymphosarcomas or nonthymic lymphomas (MST=697 days) were seen in this study. The distribution was more or less generalized, with all reticuloendothelial tissues involved to some degree, but there was little or no enlargement and involvement of the thymus. As in the case of reticulum cell sarcoma, this leukemia involved the white pulp of the spleen (Fig. 46) and expanded outward. The leukemic cell was a darker-staining, more mature lymphocyte (Fig. 47) than that seen in the earlier-occurring lymphoma which originated in the thymus. The liver involvement was generally perivascular in distribution, but tended to involve the central veins more than the periportal areas; the distribution was not nodular, either by gross or microscopic observation (Fig. 48). Very frequently the leukemic cells entered the blood stream, were seen in great numbers in the liver (Figs 49, 50), and infiltrated other organs such as the kidney (Fig. 51).

Table 1 — Type of organ involvement and location of leukemias in the RF mouse. Suggested aids for differential diagnosis

| Organ | Thymic lymphoma | Myeloid leukemia | Reticulum cell sarcoma | Nonthymic lymphoma |
|---|---|---|---|---|
| Lung | Peribronchial; perivascular; atelectasis | Emboli; thrombi; petechiae | Occasional; nodular; may be perivascular | Rare |
| Liver | Perivascular; smooth surface | Perivascular; sinusoids involved; diffuse; smooth surface | Nodular | Perivascular, especially central veins |
| Thymus | Primary | Rarely; secondary | Secondary | Rare |
| Spleen | Metastatic to red pulp; smooth surface | Begins in red pulp; smooth surface | Begins in lymphatic nodule and enlarges outwardly; nodular surface | Begins in white pulp; smooth surface |
| Heart | Routinely in basal area, also pericardium | Rarely, except within vessels | Rare | Rare |
| Sternum | Secondary invasion; pleura — cheese-like gross appearance | Necrosis of bone marrow | Rare in bone marrow | Rare |
| Lymph node | Common when generalized and slow growing; secondary | Secondary | Very common; often a primary site in a single node (*e.g.* mesenteric) | Common; primary |
| Blood | Approximately 50% | Near 100% | Rare, except in monocytic form | Occasional |
| Adrenal cortex | Occasional | High percentage | Occasional | Rare |
| Ovary and uterus | Common (50%) | Common | Occasional | Occasional |
| Kidney | Common | Common | Common | Occasional |

Erythropoiesis and megakaryocytopoiesis occurred in the leukemic spleen (Fig. 47).

**Leukemoid reaction.** — The leukemoid reaction was one of the responses of the mouse hemopoietic system which added confusion to the differential diagnosis of leukemias. The myeloproliferative tissues responded to a variety of stimuli (e.g., hemorrhage or inflammation) to produce the cells needed in each case, and this response must be differentiated from leukemia. Particularly in infectious processes, marked granulocytopoiesis occurred in the red pulp of the spleen (Figs 52, 53) and in the portal triad of the liver (Fig. 54), as well as in lymph nodes and even the adrenal cortex. While the spleen was grossly enlarged (2-3 times), each of the three developing cell lines (erythrocyte, granulocyte, and megakaryocyte) was present; despite a hypercellularity, the normal architecture of the spleen remained (Fig. 52). All stages of maturation of the granulocytes were present (Fig. 53), rather than the preponderance of only one developmental stage as found in myeloid leukemia (Figs 17, 18).

In Table 1, the type of organ involvement and locations of leukemias in the RF mouse are compared. As in most disease processes, all of the involvements were not found in each case, but the general frequency of occurrence and distribution within an organ were aids in diagnosis. Some of the organ distribution was probably related to the site of origin while other distributions possibly related to the inherent mannerisms of the leukemia in question. Table 2 lists the usual increases in cell types and the morphology as identified with the types of leukemia and leukemoid reaction.

## Tumors

**Lung.** — The most common tumor of nonreticular tissues in RF mice was in the lung (37.2% in histologically examined mice). Pulmonary adenomas have been described previously in these mice (19-22) and so will be mentioned only briefly here. The majority of tumors began in the alveolar parenchyma with a proliferation of the septae (Figs 55, 56), usually in the periphery of the lobe. Early tumors may not be detected on gross examination, but larger accumulations of tumor cells were pearly white, smooth, and well-delineated nodules on the lung surface (Figs 57, 58). An occasional difficulty arose in differentiating between small pulmonary abscesses and tumors, but the abscesses tended to be rougher and less discrete than were the tumors. As the tumors enlarged, they tended to become more papillary than tubular in morphology (Fig. 59), and were designated as papillary adenomas. Although a metastatic focus was rarely observed (usually in the regional lymph nodes), these papillary masses enlarged and became locally invasive into the bronchioles (Fig. 60) and were then

Table 2 – Increase in cell types in leukemias and leukemoid reaction in RF mice. Aids for differential diagnosis

| Dominant cell type | Thymic lymphoma | Myeloid leukemia | Reticulum cell sarcoma | Nonthymic lymphoma | Leukemoid reactions |
|---|---|---|---|---|---|
| Granulocyte | – | + | – | – | + |
| Erythrocyte | – | – | – | – | + |
| Megakaryocyte | – | – | – | – | + |
| Mature lymphocyte | – | – | – | + | + |
| Immature lymphocyte | + | – | – | – | – |
| Reticulum cell | – | – | Large pale nuclei, moderate cytoplasm, or Small, hyperchromatic, abundant cytoplasm, or Resembling fibrosarcoma | – | – |
| Cell size | Uniform (immature) | – | Pleomorphism | Uniform (mature) | – |

called papillary adenocarcinomas. Many of these tumors reached 15-20 mm in diameter and caused atelectasis, obstruction, pneumonia, and necrosis of the remaining tissue, replacing large parts of the lung parenchyma. Primary lung tumors were rarely considered to be the cause of death, but frequent lung metastases were seen from tumors of other tissues – Figure 57 shows a primary pulmonary adenoma and a metastatic focus from an osteogenic sarcoma, whose primary site was in the pelvis.

**Ovary.** – The ovary had nearly as many tumors (4.4%) as all other sites, excluding the lung (6.3%). These occurred both singly and bilaterally (Fig. 61) with, in the latter case, tumors being of the same cell type(s) in both ovaries in some instances and of different cell types in others. Most of the late-occurring tumors appeared in a combination of two or more cell types.

The early effect of radiation upon the ovary has been described previously (23-27). The immediate effect of ionizing radiation is sterilization at the lowest dose given (50 rads), with no Graafian follicles remaining in ovaries receiving 50 rads and above regardless of the type of radiation. After phagocytosis of the dead radiosensitive cells, luteal cells remained in the inner portion of the irradiated ovary, and tubular epithelial cells comprised the outer layer beneath the capsule. This stage we have designated as a pretumor or late radiation atrophy (Fig. 62). The remaining tubular elements proliferated downward from the capsule and eventually formed tubular adenomas (Figs 63, 64), which were usually considered benign. Although considerable variation existed between the gross appearance of ovarian tumors (Figs 61, 65), most of them contained some proliferation of tubular epithelial cells. Portions of some tumors had papillary manifestation (Fig. 64), but the majority were tubular in morphology.

A frequent complication in diagnosis of ovarian tumors was the concurrent appearance of hemorrhagic cysts (or hematomas) which frequently were much greater in size than the solid tumor within (Figs 65, 66). The tubular and

stromal elements are shown in higher magnification in Figure 67.

Tumors derived from granulosa cell elements of the Graafian follicle were common in the irradiated ovary, and occurred alone and in combination. Although the different elements occasionally admixed together, most nodules were more or less discrete with rather distinct boundaries of separation, each nodule usually containing a single cell type. The large nodular tumor (22 mm) in the right ovary of an 846-day-old mouse in Fig. 68 demonstrates this situation. There were nodules of granulosa-cell elements and of tubular adenomatous elements, with thrombi seen histologically (Figs 69, 70). In one portion of the granulosa cell component there was a very active area of hemosiderosis with numerous macrophages engulfing the debris (Fig. 71). Some tumors were comprised entirely of granulosa-cell components, and attempts at forming follicles were often seen (Figs 72, 73). Figures 74 and 75 show a papillary adenoma with granulosa cell elements in two separate and distinct nodules with an area of tubular adenoma elements compressed between them. The manifestations of the granulosa cell tumors were quite varied, from follicle-like structures to sarcoma-like morphology.

The luteal elements remaining after irradiation also developed into tumors of single-cell type, luteomas (Figs 76, 77). The cells were very large, with small nuclei and abundant cytoplasm, and often contained either vacuoles or fat-like materials, which were removed during processing (Fig. 77). Nearly all tumors had some remnant of luteal elements within them. A tumor composed of rather distinct nodules of luteal and granulosa cell elements, with a tubular adenoma element compressed between them, is seen in Figures 78 and 79. The different components of some mixed-cell tumors were often merged together with less discrete separation, as shown in Figures 80-82. Another mixed-cell tumor is seen in Figures 83-85, where the components are granulosa cells, luteoma, tubular adenoma, and a hemangioendothelioma. A combination of a luteoma and a papillary and tubular adenoma is seen in Figures 86 and 87. The arteries of the ovary were susceptible to polyarteritis and hyalin deposition within the vessel (which is discussed in a later section); this condition was observed in the organ whether with or without a tumor. The luteoma-tubular adenoma shown in Figures 88 and 89 had both polyarteritis and hyalinization of arterioles (Figs 90-92). Another mixed-cell combination was that of papillary and tubular adenoma elements in separate and discrete nodules (Fig. 93). An unusual observation was cholesterol clefts in a nodule of luteal cells in a mixed luteal adenoma which may have resulted from either an altered metabolism of tumor cells or hemorrhage (Fig. 94).

**Bone.** – Although not common in RF mice (0.7%), tumors of the bone were usually highly malignant osteogenic sarcomas with metastases. They were quite extensive in metastatic organ involvement, and often were considered the primary cause of death. The case shown in Figure 95 was a 489-day-old mouse with a primary tumor of the left femur. Figure 96 shows a closeup of the multiple metastatic foci in the lungs. Two different sections through the primary tumor are shown in Figures 97 and 98, with higher magnification clearly showing bone formation in the tumor (Fig. 99). Metastatic foci were also found in the liver (Fig. 100). A primary osteogenic sarcoma of the right mandible was observed in an 846-day-old mouse (Figs 101, 102); no metastases were found. A highly malignant tumor which was not diagnosed grossly, and in which the primary site was thought to be the pelvis (Fig. 103), showed metastatic foci in the lungs (Figs 104–105) with an accompanying reticulum cell sarcoma (Fig. 105). An ossifying focus was also seen in the liver (Fig. 106), and a tumor embolus was found in the right ventricle of the heart (Fig. 107).

**Pituitary gland.** – Adenomas of the pituitary gland were diagnosed in 1.4% of the nontreated mice and reached sizes of 8-10 mm. Presumptive external signs of a pituitary gland tumor were seen as the skin was reflected and the cranial vessels were observed to be markedly distended (Fig. 108); in another mouse with a pituitary tumor, an elevation of the frontal and parietal bones is viewed laterally (Fig. 109). Most of the tumors were solid, but some were cystic, even hemorrhagic (Fig. 110). The hemorrhage was largely lost during processing for histological examination (Fig. 111). This particular tumor differed from those usually observed by having large numbers of giant cells and considerable pleomorphism (Fig. 112), rather than having very uniform chromophobe cells. A majority of the cells in most tumors were quite uniform in size and staining properties; they were relatively pale, with a moderate amount of cytoplasm, and were negative for granule stainings by Gude's modification of the Martin-Mallory technique (6). Although some cellular atypia and giantism are seen, these morphological characteristics and the granule-staining are demonstrated in the solid tumor in Figures 109 and 113–117.

**Mammary gland.** – Tumors of the mammary gland were diagnosed in 1.4% of the female mice and occurred in association with both front and rear limbs. An 847-day-old mouse died with a 30-mm subcutaneous mass in the right inguinal area (Figs 118, 119). The firm nodular mass was white on the cut surface and of cheesy consistency; large necrotic areas were seen in the tumor mass (Figs 119, 120). The glandlike structures contained numerous mitotic figures and were moderately invasive (Figs 120, 121); the diagnosis was adenocarcinoma. Multiple metastatic foci, which closely resembled the primary tumor in morphology and cytology, were found in the lung (Figs 122, 123). In a 708-day-old mouse, a large (30 X 400 mm) subcutaneous mass was found in the left axillary area (Fig. 124). The mass had elements of tubular formation (Figs 125, 126), but the dominant components were fibrous with whorl formations and numerous mitotic figures throughout the tumor (Figs 126, 127). The diagnosis was adenofibrosarcoma. In one area of the tumor were found deposits of extracellular hyalin material of undetermined etiology (Fig. 128).

**Uterus.** – Uterine neoplasia was found in 0.9% of the mice, with considerable variation in cell type. An 804-day-old mouse had a 20-mm blood-filled mass beginning in the cervical area and involving most of the right uterine horn (Fig. 129). The tumor was composed primarily of proliferating endothelial elements with entrapped blood (with numerous red and white blood cells) and numerous thrombi (Figs 130, 131); a diagnosis of hemangioendothelioma was made. Another mouse (941 days old) had a 12 X 20 mm firm mass in the left horn of the uterus (Fig. 132). The tumor was composed of proliferating epithelial cells which formed bizarre pseudoducts with dense supportive tissue (Figs 133, 134). The cells were quite anaplastic with a high nuclear-cytoplasmic ratio and large nuclei; accumulations of cells and cellular debris were found in some of the ductlike structures (Fig. 135). The diagnosis was fibroadenocarcinoma.

Various forms of proliferative change in the uterine mucosa and associated structures were common, and ranged from mild cystic hyperplasia to various polypoid formations in most middle-aged to old animals. A papillary cystadenoma in the uterus of a 760-day-old animal was found microscopically (Figs 136, 137). The cells appeared to be mature and were not considered malignant. A cystadenomatous polyp of the uterus was an incidental finding in a 617-day-old mouse dying with myeloid leukemia (Figs 138, 139). The mass protruded into the lumen of the uterus with the dominant cell type resembling the epithelium of the uterus; some tubular structures were necrotic (Fig. 139). An unusual tumor of the uterus was found in an 828-day-old mouse dying with reticulum cell sarcoma. The mass was quite vascular (Fig. 140) and appeared to be of epithelial origin (Fig. 141). Although the mice were virgin, this mass resembled that of a deciduoma from the remnants of placentation, and the tumor was so diagnosed and confirmed by consultant pathologists.

**Liver.** — The occasional hepatic tumors found in RF female mice (0.7%) were usually diagnosed histologically rather than at necropsy.

A 572-day-old mouse had a large hepatoma (Fig. 142), the cells of which closely resembled liver parenchymal cells although they were larger, with more cytoplasm and more variation in size. They tended to form closely packed cords and sheets with dilated sinusoidal spaces between the cells. A reticulum cell sarcoma was also diagnosed in this liver. One of the unusual observations associated with the hepatoma was the appearance of bizarre cystic ductlike structures at the periphery of the tumor (Fig. 143); this was not commonly seen in either irradiated or nonirradiated livers. Previously, Clapp and Craig had reported similar lesions in RF male mice after treatment with diethylnitrosamine (DEN) (19). They described a proliferation of small "oval cells" of uncertain origin in the portal triad areas of the liver during the DEN treatment period, and these cells coalesced to form what some have called a cholangioma. They did not consider these malignant, but very large cysts did develop in most livers of older DEN-treated mice, with pressure necrosis resulting in the destruction of much of the liver parenchyma. The female mouse in this study received no similar chemical treatment, and the etiology of this unusual lesion is uncertain. While one might suggest that the proliferation followed biochemical alterations within the tumor tissue, the reverse process was observed in DEN-treatment where proliferation of "oval cells" and cyst-formation preceded hepatoma development.

Another hepatoma was diagnosed, concurrently with a reticulum cell sarcoma, in a 759-day-old mouse (Fig. 144). The tumor cells were more nearly the size of normal liver parenchymal cells, although the nuclei were lighter staining (Fig. 145). The sinusoidal spaces were distended more than normal tissue, and small mononuclear cells and cellular debris were seen in them (Fig. 146). Within the tumor mass, eosinophilic spherical deposits were seen in the cytoplasm of a large number of cells. The etiology of these deposits was undetermined.

Hemangioendothelioma of the liver was observed occasionally. A 707-day-old mouse died with generalized reticulum cell sarcoma and multiple liver abscesses. One lobe of the liver had a mass (Fig. 147) of small endothelial cells which had proliferated rapidly and obliterated the parenchyma. They tended to line enclosed spaces which were filled with blood cells (Figs 148, 149). This tumor differed somewhat from the hemangioendothelioma of the uterus (Figs 130, 131) and from those induced in RF males by dimethylnitrosamine (20-22), and was classified as a variant hemangioendotheliomata.

**Adrenal.** — One mouse dying at 848 days of age had a pheochromocytoma of the adrenal medulla, which was detected histologically. The cells were large, with abundant

cytoplasm, and formed cord-like structures (Figs 150, 151). Pressure necrosis upon the cortex was obvious, with a marked reduction in thickness.

**Skin and associated appendages.** — Squamous cell carcinomas were found occasionally in the skin and associated structures. One mouse had an ulcerated mass at the base of the right concha extending over the cranium to the midline (Fig. 152). The tumor was very invasive, extending subcutaneously (Fig. 153), with many areas of mild to severe anaplasia and keratin production (Fig. 154); numerous mitotic figures were observed, but no invasion into the cranium was seen. At the base of the tail, another mouse (994 days old) had a 7-mm squamous cell carcinoma which also had areas of keratin production and foci of anaplastic cells (Figs 155, 156). Another mouse died at 648 days with a squamous cell carcinoma of the vulva (Figs 157, 158). This tumor was very invasive and quite anaplastic with little keratin production. None of these tumors showed evidence of metastasis.

**Harderian gland.** — Tumors of this periorbital gland occurred in 1.0% of irradiated mice although none were diagnosed in controls in this study. A 603-day-old mouse had a unilateral adenocarcinoma of the Harderian gland (Fig. 159). This tumor expanded subcutaneously, closing the right eye and ulcerating through the skin. The tumor exerted pressure on the turbinate bones of the nasal cavity, causing necrosis of the epithelial lining and of the bones (Fig. 160). The tumor cells were hyperchromatic with moderate cytoplasm, and formed glandlike structures where the tumor was more mature (Fig. 161). This adenocarcinoma invaded into muscle tissues (Fig. 162) but no metastases were found. A more differentiated adenoma was found in a mouse that died at 912 days of age (Fig. 163). Normal Harderian glandular tissue can be seen around the tumor which developed a papillary appearance and was neither as anaplastic nor as invasive as the previous tumor.

**Other tumor sites.** — The primary sites of some tumors were not identified. A 637-day-old mouse died with an anaplastic adenocarcinoma in the lung (Figs 164, 165) with a metastatic focus in the mediastinal lymph node (Fig. 166) and two foci in the left ventricle of the heart (Fig. 167). The primary site was probably the lung, but this is unusual in RF mice (20-22). A 656-day-old mouse died with generalized reticulum cell sarcoma and had multiple 20- to 30-mm masses in the abdomen (Fig. 168). At necropsy the kidney was suggested as a possible primary site, with abdominal metastases. The tumor was a moderately differentiated adenocarcinoma (Fig. 169), but the primary site was not definitely determined.

A 35-mm cystic, polypoid abdominal mass was found in a 762-day-old mouse (Figs 170, 171). Although the tumor extended into the inguinal area and might have been considered grossly as a mammary tumor, the mass originated within the abdominal cavity and extended outwardly, involving the peritoneum. The center of the mass was necrotic, but a typical cellular configuration is shown in Fig. 172. The cells concentrated in nodules around what appeared to be endothelial tissue. The hypochromatic tumor cells were juvenile, with a high nuclear-cytoplasmic ratio, prominent nucleoli, high mitotic index, and epithelial-like appearance (Fig. 173). Cellular necrosis was seen in rapidly growing areas. This tumor was diagnosed as a mesothelioma and may have originated from the peritoneum (consultant pathologists confirmed this diagnosis).

## Nonneoplastic Diseases

### Cardiovascular Processes

**Auricular thromboses.** — Either one or occasionally both auricles of the heart became markedly distended with a firm, light-colored mass (6.8% incidence in controls) as seen in Figure 174. The thrombus was usually attached to the wall of the auricle and ranged from near total occlusion of the lumen (Fig. 175) to a smaller accumulation with partial occlusion (Fig. 176), which may be detectable only at histologic examination. The thrombus is "onion-skin" in histological appearance as the alternating layers of inflammatory cells overlay the fibrin and red blood cell accumulation. Auricular thrombosis does not appear to be associated with polyarteritis of the coronary vessels or other vascular lesions. The 707-day-old mouse shown in Figure 147 has auricular thrombosis, liver abscesses, reticulum cell sarcoma of the Peyer's patches, and a hemangioendothelioma of the liver, demonstrating the variety of serious diseases which can be observed in a single mouse.

**Ventricular thromboses.** — Ventricular thromboses were found occasionally in RF females, but not as frequently as auricular thromboses. Most often they were much smaller, and were detected histologically (Figs 177, 178). This 744-day-old mouse (Figs 177, 178) also had concurrent auricular thrombosis and cardiac abscesses, although there does not appear to be a correlation between the three diseases.

**Polyarteritis (periarteritis).** — Unlike the manifestation of polyarteritis nodosa in humans, which results in nodular formation in the mesenteric vessels of the abdominal viscera (28), this disease was most commonly seen in older mice and was most prevalent in the coronary vessels at the base of the heart. It often involved arteries of the kidney, uterus, spleen, and ovary, and has been seen in nearly all organs of the body. Polyarteritis was found in 13.6% of the control mice in this study and was described previously by Upton *et al.* (29). It involved the external portions of the arteries (tunica media and tunica adventitia) and periarterial tissue, with a proliferative inflammatory response. With progress of the lesion, more layers become involved until the entire vessel may contain inflammatory cells and be markedly thickened. Many vessels throughout the body, or only a few in a single organ, may be involved.

An 848-day-old mouse died with a generalized reticulum cell sarcoma and a nodular enlargement of the thoracic and abdominal aorta (Fig. 179). A generalized polyarteritis of the aorta and branching arteries was seen, with the largest of the nodules being an aneurysm containing a thrombus (Figs 180, 181). The aorta and most of the associated branching arteries were involved in this inflammatory and proliferative process (Fig. 182). Figure 183 shows another section from the same general area with two vessels cut in cross-section and one longitudinally, with all three vessels undergoing the polyarteritic and proliferative changes; an occluding thrombus is also seen in one artery. Figure 184 is a higher magnification than Figure 182 and shows the proliferative response and markedly thickened vessel walls, with inflammatory cells infiltrating primarily the outer layers and the perivascular tissues. This mouse also had cystic kidneys (Fig. 185) and moderate glomerulosclerosis with polyarteritis of the small vessels (Fig. 186). One arteriole was nearly occluded. The inflammatory cells were primarily mononuclear, with a preponderance of lymphocytes and some plasma cells. Connective tissue stains showed an increase of collagen in the inflammatory regions, especially at the periphery of the lesion, and an increase in mucopolysaccharides was demonstrated by PAS stain.

When polyarteritis involved the coronary vessels, the picture was that of necrosis with nonproliferative inflammation of the adventitia, perivascular tissue, and often muscle fibers (Fig. 187), in contrast to the extensive proliferation of the media and adventitia in vessels other than the coronary arteries. Although the coronary vessels at the base of the heart were most often involved, changes in other arterioles supplying the myocardium were also seen (Figs 188, 189). Chondrification of the coronary vessels, a degenerative change found occasionally in older mice, accompanied the polyarteritic change (Fig. 188). Proliferation of the media was seen in the coronary vessels (Fig. 190), accompanied by the more common necrotizing and nonproliferative inflammatory change of the myocardium.

Other organs were also involved. Figure 191 shows periarteritis of several arterioles of the adrenal gland from an 809-day-old mouse. Concurrently there is a deposition of hyalin-like eosinophilic material immediately beneath the endothelial surface. Although the hyalin deposits may be observed concurrently with periarteritis, the relative noninflammatory appearance suggested that the two diseases may be unrelated. Most cases of periarteritis, even when severe, did not have hyalin deposits, while small arterioles and capillaries were often markedly thickened with hyalin despite very little inflammatory or proliferative response. Both of these diseases were seen concurrently in the spleen from the mouse shown in Figures 192 and 193.

**Phlebitis.** — A severe phlebitis was seen in a 506-day-old mouse with an associated severe polyarteritis of the arteries of the femoral area (Figs 194, 195). The pathogenesis and correlation between these two lesions was not established, but the phlebitis of the femoral vein may have resulted from the extension of the inflammatory periarteritis of the femoral arteries.

**Pneumonia**. — Mice were maintained in conventional housing facilities with excellent husbandry procedures to maintain animal cleanliness; consequently, few infectious diseases were observed. Acute bronchopneumonia was seen occasionally (Figs 196, 197) with the infiltrate usually located peribronchially and perivascularly and following the "respiratory tree." The bronchial passageways were often filled with pus, with plasma cells and other mononuclear cells infiltrating around the bronchiolar passageways. Distribution was most often confined to one lobe, but on occasion several lobes, and even bilateral distribution, were seen.

**Abscesses**. — Abscesses were found occasionally in most organs of the body. Abscesses were seen in the myocardium (Fig. 198) while multiple liver abscesses were found in a 715-day-old mouse (Fig. 199) and are shown in higher magnifications in Fig. 200. The lung tumor seen grossly in Fig. 199 was a papillary adenoma (Fig. 201).

## Metabolic and Degenerative Diseases

**Glomerulosclerosis**. — This lesion was found quite early in RF mice and it has been suggested that it occurs earlier following irradiation (6). Deposits of eosinophilic material occurred within the capillary loops of the glomerulus and, with an increase in time, filled most of the glomeruli with homogenous material (Fig. 202). Intratubular casts were observed in advanced cases (Fig. 202) and many glomeruli apparently had become nonfunctional. Due to an interference with the blood supply to the cortical areas, the surface of the kidney became pitted and scarred. Glomerulosclerosis was graded into four categories — negative, slight, moderate, and severe. In general, most of the animals surviving 30 days or longer postirradiation had beginning glomerulosclerotic change. The subjective evaluation of glomerulosclerosis was based on the degenerative and noninflammatory changes which were usually rather consistent within a kidney; the evaluation was determined from change in approximately two-thirds of the glomeruli in the histological sections. The designation of *slight* was assigned when the majority of the glomeruli had definite hyalinization and thickening of the capillary walls but less than one-third of the mesangium was occupied with the deposits. *Moderate* was used when one- to two-thirds of the mesangium was involved, and the *severe* grade was given when two-thirds or more of the volume of the glomerular tuft was affected in a majority of the glomeruli. Figures 202–204 demonstrate severe glomerulosclerosis. Figure 204 shows an interesting digression from the usual pattern in which only the capillary loops were involved. In this case, deposits occurred outside the loops in Bowman's capsule where glomerular filtrate is collected. There is an increased cellularity in this glomerulus, but pressure necro-

sis and other degenerative changes are not evident. We have reported recently that the occurrence of severe glomerulosclerosis reduces the risk of dying with reticulum cell sarcoma by a factor of 2 to 3, while not altering nonlymphatic tumor incidences (30,31).

**Arterial hyalinization**. — In contrast with the inflammatory process which we have described as polyarteritis (periarteritis), deposits of hyalinlike material within the walls of the arteries did not appear as an inflammatory process. The deposit was seen in the media immediately beneath the endothelium (Figs. 191, 193). The muscular layers and the externa were pushed outward away from the lumen of the vessel and some proliferation occurred in these layers; the lumen may also become smaller. This deposit may be seen with periarteritis or more often in the absence of polyarteritis in a particular artery. The occurrence of the two processes does not appear to have an obvious correlation. The eosinophilic material is amorphous and may be found in arteries of most any organ; the most common were the spleen, uterus (Fig. 205), and kidney. Hyalin was seen in a spermatic artery of an older male RF mouse in another study (Fig. 206). By special staining techniques the material is PAS- and fibrin-positive, and negative to amyloid stains. The etiology of this disease is uncertain, but may be related to the autoimmune diseases periarteritis and glomerulosclerosis, as has been suggested previously (30, 31).

**Chondrification, calcification, and ossification**. — Chondrification was occasionally seen at the base of the valvular attachments of the heart in older mice. In an 819-day-old mouse, chondrification of the heart valve was seen in association with chronic myocarditis, primarily of lymphocytic infiltration (Fig. 207). These lesions may have been of independent origin as most occurrences of chondrification were not associated with inflammation.

Calcification was seen as a development secondary to hemorrhage of long standing, as shown in the adrenal medulla of a 526-day-old mouse (Fig. 208).

Extensive ectopic ossification of the spleen, with "metastatic" ossification to the liver and left ovary, was found in a 558-day-old mouse. The lesion in the spleen involved both the white and red pulp and the entire splenic architecture had been destroyed (Figs 209, 210). Several metastatic nodules were seen in the ovary; the largest is shown in Fig. 211. Multiple nodules were also found in the liver (Fig. 212). The etiology of the lesion was undetermined, but it was considered metabolic in origin rather than a malignancy.

**Sternal necrosis**. — In nearly all older mice (over 15–18 months of age), necrosis was observed in the sternebrae. This change appeared first in the intersternebral region as a necrosis with acellularity, and the bone and cartilage became an amorphous eosinophilic mass (Fig. 213). With time and advancement of the disease, the areas of endochondral ossification and chondrification in the sternebral bodies also became necrotic as seen in Figures 214 and 215. The severity of the lesion was age-dependent and progressed from isolated areas of necrosis, with deposits of the homogenous material, until a majority of the inter-sternebral space was obliterated and replaced with the necrotic eosinophilic material. Quantifying of this age-dependent change has not been accomplished, but this may be an asymptomatic parameter which could be evaluated for use in measuring the aging process.

**Uterine hyperplasia**. — The uteri of most mice 12 months of age and older had a marked endometrial hyperplasia which frequently included proliferation of the supportive tissues. This change was very consistent and was considered normal for the aging mouse. There were frequent spurious proliferations of the endometrial ele-ments with accompanying microscopic cysts, which were often quite extensive and often detectable without incision into the uterus. Examples of this lesion in its mild form, with accompanying microcysts, are shown in Figures 216 and 217. This aging lesion was not usually inflammatory in nature, although occasional macrophages and polymorpho-nuclear cells were found in the lumina of the cysts accompanying cellular debris. The supportive tissues be-neath the serosal surface also proliferated, and increased vascularity of the tissues was obvious.

**Miscellaneous observations**. — Bladder calculi, one of which is shown in Figures 218 and 219, were rare in RF mice. A 715-day-old mouse had calculi of the urinary bladder, with a corresponding thickening of the epithelial wall and associated granulomatous inflammation.

Anomalies of organs were occasionally found in RF mice; the most common was a displacement of the portal vein anterior to the duodenum, the lesion being found incidentally at necropsy. No obvious detrimental effects accompanied the change. Other anomalies were rare. A 770-day-old mouse had a 20 × 40 mm distension of the left kidney, which was fluid-filled (Fig. 220). Aplasia of the kidney cortex was evident, with only a thin layer of cortical cells remaining.

Hydronephrosis was rarely seen and ranged from early changes to severe distension of the kidney pelvis, with associated pressure upon the parenchyma.

# DISEASE INCIDENCES

Necropsy and gross observation of all 526 control mice revealed no difference in incidence, for any of the diseases studied, between proton and X-ray sham-irradiated mice. Therefore, data on all control mice were pooled for evaluation.

All mice in the study were carefully examined even if they were severely autolyzed, which was the case for 99 of the animals. The remaining 427 mice were examined histologically, totally or in part, the latter being the case when some specific tissue or organ had deteriorated beyond

any possibility of such examination. Of the 427, histo-logical examination of 311 specifically included lungs, heart, kidneys, liver, spleen, ovaries, uterus, and lymph nodes. We felt it possible that stronger inferences could be made regarding the effects of ionizing radiation if the two subgroups of histologically examined mice were used as a basis of comparison with our experimental (irradiated) mice; therefore we first made a comparison of leukemia and tumor incidences in the two subgroups of control mice with the entire control population (Table 3). Only minor, insignificant differences were found, except that an increase in incidences of neoplasms was found in the histologically examined subgroups, as expected, since we observed early neoplasms microscopically which would not have been diagnosed by gross examination only. However, only reticulum cell sarcoma and lung tumors showed an increase. We therefore concluded that, in discussing the effects observed, we could confidently utilize the histologically examined group of 311 and 427 mice interchangeably with the total population of 526 controls.

Incidences of thymic lymphoma (4.0%) and myeloid leukemia (0.9%) are within the range of previous reports in RF females (5, 8, 10-14, 32, 33). Females usually have a slightly but consistently higher incidence of thymic lym-phoma and lower incidence of myeloid leukemia than observed in males. We observed over 56% incidence of reticulum cell sarcoma in nontreated females and 6% incidence of nonthymic lymphoma; in previous reports (loc. cit.), these have been listed collectively as "other leukemias" and were somewhat lower in total incidence (35-40%).

Tumor incidences were most common in the lung (37.2%) and ovary (4.4%), with only 6.3% in all other sites; the lung-tumor incidence was nearly twice that reported previously for RF females (5, 8, 14, 32), and was similar to incidences (39%) reported for RF males (19-22). Tumors of other organs were uncommon, but most organs did develop an occasional tumor; the pituitary and the breast were the only organs with incidences >1%. Tumors of other sites were not considered individually in the subgroup given extensive histological examination.

In Table 4 we have listed the total number of mice with all types of leukemias and tumors, and have compared the number of leukemia-bearing and tumor-bearing mice. In only four mice were two different leukemias diagnosed concurrently, while 45 mice bore multiple primary tumors at different sites. Consequently, when incidence was cor-rected for multiple diseases, 66% of all nontreated mice were leukemic and 44% were tumor-bearing.

In Table 5 are listed diagnoses of some of the nonneoplastic diseases which were recognized primarily upon histological examination; consequently, only the two histologically examined subgroups were used for evaluating these diseases. Auricular thrombosis was found in 6.8% and bronchopneumonia in 9.4% of the histologically examined mice, while polyarteritis was seen in 13.6% of the cases.

Table 3 – Leukemia and tumor incidences in 526 nontreated (control) RF female mice

| Disease | Gross observation all mice[a] | | Histologic examination | | | |
| | | | 427 mice[b] | | 311 mice[c] | |
| | Incidence (%) | MST[d] (days) | Incidence (%) | MST[d] (days) | Incidence (%) | MST[d] (days) |
|---|---|---|---|---|---|---|
| **LEUKEMIA** | | | | | | |
| Thymic lymphoma | 3.6 (19/526) | 423 | 4.0 (17/427) | 455 | 4.2 (13/311) | 453 |
| Myeloid leukemia | 1.1 (6/526) | 591 | 0.9 (4/427) | 622 | 0 (0/311) | |
| Reticulum cell sarcoma | 51.9 (273/526) | 655 | 56.2 (240/427) | 659 | 50.5 (157/311) | 646 |
| Nonthymic lymphoma | 6.5 (34/526) | 699 | 7.0 (30/427) | 697 | 5.5 (17/311) | 656 |
| **TUMORS OF:** | | | | | | |
| Lung | 31.9 (168/526) | 700 | 37.2 (159/427) | 705 | 38.6 (120/311) | 704 |
| Ovary | 3.8 (20/526) | 696 | 4.4 (19/427) | 702 | 4.5 (14/311) | 723 |
| Other sites | 5.7 (30/526) | 706 | 6.3 (27/427) | 721 | 6.4 (20/311) | 743 |
| Pituitary | 1.3 (7/526) | 677 | 1.4 (6/427) | 676 | | |
| Liver | 0.8 (4/526) | 698 | 0.7 (3/427) | 792 | | |
| Uterus | 0.8 (4/526) | 831 | 0.9 (4/427) | 831 | | |
| Bone | 0.6 (3/526) | 594 | 0.7 (3/427) | 594 | | |
| Breast | 1.1 (6/526) | 794 | 1.4 (6/427) | 794 | | |
| Kidney | 0.4 (2/526) | 754 | 0.5 (2/427) | 754 | | |
| Adrenal | 0.2 (1/526) | 624 | 0.2 (1/427) | 624 | | |
| Ear | 0.2 (1/526) | 754 | 0.2 (1/427) | 754 | | |
| Abdomen | 0.4 (5/526) | 524 | 0.5 (2/427) | 524 | | |

[a] All 526 mice were necropsied for gross observation of disease incidence.

[b] A majority of the tissues from 427 of the mice were examined histologically.

[c] In 311 of the 427 mice, lungs, ovaries, kidneys, heart, liver, spleen, uterus, and lymph nodes were examined histologically, and, in some cases, other organs as well.

[d] Mean survival time.

Incidences of polyarteritis and hyalinization of arterioles were compared only in the extensively examined group and were 18% and 14%, respectively. Glomerulosclerosis was examined in both groups and was graded histologically as slight, moderate, or severe, in a manner similar to that of Gude *et al.* (6). Similar incidences and mean survival times were observed in both groups; a majority of mice examined histologically had some degree of glomerulosclerosis, 95% of the extensively examined mice having some involvement (Table 5). We have reported recently an interrelation between glomerulosclerosis, polyarteritis, and arterial hyalinization and the risk of occurrence of reticulum cell sarcoma (30, 31). Severe glomerulosclerosis is associated with a fourfold increase in the risk of polyarteritis and an eightfold increase in the risk of arterial hyalinization. In addition, severe glomerulosclerosis, alone or in combination with polyarteritis or hyalinization, decreases the risk of reticulum cell sarcoma by a factor of 2 to 3 in nontreated mice. The interrelation of these diseases and their causality is now the subject of intensive studies. Mice with severe cases die, and are observed, earlier because severe glomerulosclerosis is the primary cause of death; lesser involvement is an incidental finding in mice dying from other causes. Most of these nonneoplastic diseases are relatively late-occurring, usually after mice have reached 20 months or more of age. Other diseases were either of too low incidence or were not considered in sufficient quantitative detail to be included in incidence evaluations.

Table 4 — Total leukemia and tumor incidence in 526 nontreated
(control) RF female mice

| Disease | Observed incidence in all mice[a] (%) | Incidence in histologically examined mice | |
|---|---|---|---|
| | | 427 mice[b] (%) | 311 mice[c] (%) |
| All leukemias | 62.3 (328/526) | 67.2 (287/427) | 60.1 (187/311) |
| Number of leukemia mice; incidence corrected for animals with two different types of leukemia | | 66.3 (283/427) | |
| All tumors | 47.1 (248/526) | 54.6 (233/427) | |
| Number of tumor-bearing mice; incidence corrected for animals with two or more primary tumors of different sites | | 44.0 (188/427) | |

[a]All 526 mice were necropsied.
[b]Histologic examination of tissues from 427 of the mice.
[c]Histologic examination of tissues from certain organs (lungs, ovaries, kidneys, heart, liver, spleen, uterus, and lymph nodes, and in some cases other organs as well) from 311 of the 427 mice.

Table 5 — Incidences of nonneoplastic disease in two
groups of histologically examined nontreated
(control) RF female mice

| Disease | Group I (427 mice)[a] | | Group 2 (311 mice)[b] | |
|---|---|---|---|---|
| | Incidence (%) | MST[c] (days) | Incidence (%) | MST[c] (days) |
| Auricular thrombosis | 6.8 (29/427) | 666 | | |
| Bronchopneumonia | 9.4 (40/427) | 672 | | |
| Polyarteritis | 13.6 (58/427) | 674 | 18.0 (56/311) | 669 |
| Hyalin (arterial) | | | 14.1 (44/311) | 660 |
| Glomerulosclerosis | | | | |
| Slight | 21.5 (92/427) | 579 | 26.7 (83/311) | 569 |
| Moderate | 29.3 (125/427) | 675 | 31.8 (99/311) | 675 |
| Severe | 33.0 (141/427) | 638 | 36.6 (144/311) | 628 |

[a]Histologic examination of tissues.
[b]Histologic examination of tissues from certain organs (lungs, ovaries, kidneys, heart, liver, spleen, uterus, and lymph nodes, and in some cases other organs as well) from 311 of the 427 mice.
[c]Mean survival time.

# Summary

While the RF mouse has been used as the experimental animal in many reported studies, variation in experimental procedures and methodology of observation by the various investigators has made comparison of results difficult. To provide baseline pathology data for future experiments, we have described in this report diseases found in an experimental population of 3135 female RF mice, and have included incidences of the diseases found in the untreated controls.

Four types of leukemias (thymic lymphoma, myeloid leukemia, reticulum cell sarcoma, and nonthymic lymphoma) are described, with incidences in untreated mice of 4.0, 0.9, 56.2, and 7.0%, respectively. The most common primary sites for nonreticular tumors were lung (37.2%) and ovary (4.4%), with tumors of all other sites totaling 6.3%. Other diseases of the RF mouse include auricular thrombosis (6.8%), bronchopneumonia (9.4%), and polyarteritis (13.6%) in the 427-mouse subgroup. Incidences of other diseases in the 311-mouse subgroup were polyarteritis (18.0%), arterial hyalinization (14.1%), and glomerulosclerosis (slight, 26.7%; moderate, 31.8%; severe, 36.6%).

In irradiated mice, glomerulosclerosis was seen in most kidneys beyond 30 days postirradiation, and was a noninflammatory deposition of eosinophilic material in the mesangium of the glomerular tuft.

Gross and histopathologic photographs are included to illustrate the diseases described.

# References

1. T. B. Dunn. Normal and pathologic anatomy of the reticular tissue in laboratory mice. *J. Nat. Cancer. Inst.*, **14**: 1281–1433 (1954).

2. R. G. Gottschalk and J. Furth. Polycythemia with features of Cushing's syndrome produced by luteomas. *Acta. Haematol.*, **5**: 100–123 (1951).

3. J. Furth and J. Moshman. On the specificity of hypervolemia and congestive changes in tumor-bearing mice. *Cancer Res.*, **11**: 543–551 (1951).

4. J. Furth and J. B. Kahn. Experimental radiation-induced ovarian tumors: Adenocarcinoma with hypervolemia. *Acta. Unio Int. Contra Cancrum*, **7**: 827–830 (1952).

5. A. C. Upton, F. F. Wolff, J. Furth, and A. W. Kimball. A comparison of the induction of myeloid and lymphoid leukemias in X-radiated RF mice. *Cancer Res.*, **18**: 842–848 (1958).

6. W. D. Gude and A. C. Upton. Spontaneous glomerulosclerosis in aging RF mice. *J. Gerontol.*, **15**: 373–376 (1960).

7. A. C. Upton. Ionizing radiation and aging. *Gerontologia*, **4**: 162–176 (1960).

8. A. C. Upton, M. A. Kastenbaum, and J. W. Conklin. Age-specific death rates of mice exposed to ionizing radiation and radiomimetric agents. In *Cellular Basis and Aetiology of Late Somatic Effects of Ionizing Radiation.* Academic Press, London, 1962, pp. 285–297.

9. G. E. Cosgrove, A. C. Upton, C. C. Congdon, D. G. Doherty, K. W. Christenberry, and D. G. Gosslee. Late somatic effects of X-radiation in mice treated with AET and isologous bone marrow. *Radiat. Res.*, **21**: 550–574 (1964).

10. A. C. Upton. Comparative aspects of carcinogenesis by ionizing radiation. *Nat. Cancer Inst. Monogr.*, **14**: 221–242 (1964).

11. A. C. Upton, V. K. Jenkins, and J. W. Conklin. Myeloid leukemia in the mouse. *Ann. N. Y. Acad. Sci.*, **144**: 189–201 (1964).

12. G. E. Cosgrove and A. C. Upton. Pathology of the reticulo-endothelial system. In *The Pathology of Laboratory Animals* (W. E. Ribelin and John R. McCoy, eds.). Charles C Thomas, Springfield, 1965, pp. 1–25.

13. A. C. Upton, V. K. Jenkins, H. E. Walburg, Jr., R. L. Tyndall, J. W. Conklin, and N. Wald. Observations on viral, chemical, and radiation-induced myeloid and lymphoid leukemias in RF mice. *Nat. Cancer. Inst.. Mongr.* **22**: 329–347 (1965).

14. E. B. Darden, Jr., G. E. Cosgrove, A. C. Upton, K. W. Christenberry, J. W. Conklin, and M. L. Davis. Late somatic effects in female RF/Un mice irradiated with single doses of 14-MeV fast neutrons. *Int. J. Radiat. Biol.*, **12**: 435–452 (1967).

15. A. C. Upton, M. L. Randolph, and J. W. Conklin. Late effects of fast neutrons and gamma rays in mice as influenced by the dose rate of irradiation: Life shortening. *Radiat. Res.*, **32**: 493–509 (1967).

16. E. B. Darden, Jr., K. W. Christenberry, J. J. Beauchamp, R. S. Bender, M. C. Jernigan, J. W. Conklin, and A. C. Upton. Comparison of 60-MeV protons and 300-kVp X-rays for induction of lens opacities in RF mice. *Radiat. Res.*, **43**: 598–612 (1970).

17. R. S. Bender and E. B. Darden, Jr. A broad-beam biology facility for proton irradiation at the Oak Ridge Isochronous Cyclotron. *Radiat. Res.* **41**: 247–258 (1970).

18. N. K. Clapp, E. B. Darden, Jr., and M. C. Jernigan. Relative effects of whole-body sublethal doses of 60-MeV protons and 300-kVp X rays on disease incidences in RF mice. *Radiat. Res.*, in press.

19. N. K. Clapp and A. W. Craig. Carcinogenic effects of diethylnitrosamine in RF mice. *J. Nat. Cancer Inst.*, **39**: 903–916 (1967).

20. N. K. Clapp, A. W. Craig, and R. E. Toya. Pulmonary and hepatic oncogenesis during treatment of male RF mice with

dimethylnitrosamine. *J. Nat. Cancer Inst.*, **41**: 1213–1227 (1968).

21. N. K. Clapp and R. E. Toya. Effect of cumulative dose and dose rate on dimethylnitrosamine oncogenesis in RF mice. *J. Nat. Cancer Inst.*, **45**: 495–498, 1970.

22. N. K. Clapp, R. L. Tyndall, and J. A. Otten. Differences in tumor types and organ susceptibility in BALB/c and RF mice following dimethylnitrosamine and diethylnitrosamine. *Cancer Res.*, **31**: 196–198 (1971).

23. J. Furth and M. C. Boon. Induction of ovarian tumors in mice by X-rays. *Cancer Res.*, **7**: 241–246 (1947).

24. T. Bali and J. Furth. Morphological and biological characteristics of X-ray-induced transplantable ovarian tumors. *Cancer Res.*, **9**: 449–472 (1949).

25. J. Furth and O. B. Furth. Neoplastic diseases produced in mice by general irradiation with X-rays. I. Incidence and types of neoplasms. *Amer. J. Cancer*, **28**: 54–65 (1936).

26. A. C. Upton, A. W. Kimball, J. Furth, K. W. Christenberry, and W. H. Benedict. Some delayed effects of atom-bomb radiations in mice. *Cancer Res.*, **20**: 1–62 (1960).

27. J. Furth and J. S. Butterworth. Neoplastic diseases occurring among mice subjected to general irradiation with X-rays. II. Ovarian tumor and associated lesions. *Amer. J. Cancer*, **28**: 66–95 (1936).

28. P. M. Zeek, C. C. Smith, and J. C. Weeter. Studies on periarteritis nodosa. III. The differentiation between the vascular lesions of periarteritis nodosa and hypersensitivity. *Amer. J. Pathol.*, **24**: 889 (1948).

29. A. C. Upton, J. W. Conklin, G. E. Cosgrove, W. D. Gude, and E. B. Darden. Necrotizing polyarteritis in aging RF mice. *Lab. Invest.*, **16**: 483–487 (1967).

30. J. M. Yuhas and N. K. Clapp. Incidence of leukemia and nonlymphatic tumors in mice with glomerulosclerosis and allied disorders. *J. Nat. Cancer Inst.*, **48**: 367–373 (1972).

31. N. K. Clapp and J. M. Yuhas. A suggested correlation between radiation-induced immunosuppression and radiogenic leukemia in mice. *J. Nat. Cancer Inst.*, in press.

32. A. C. Upton, M. L. Randolph, and J. W. Conklin. Late effects of fast neutrons and gamma-rays in mice as influenced by the dose rate of irradiation: Induction of neoplasia. *Radiat. Res.*, **41**: 467–491 (1970).

33. M. L. Davis, G. E. Cosgrove, H. E. Walburg, Jr., and E. Leach. The incidence of major diseases of control, untreated mouse strains used in life-span studies in the Biology Division. ORNL-TM-3714, April 1972.

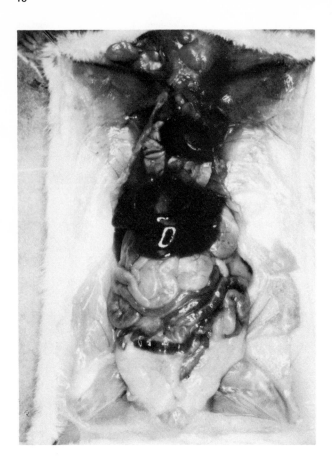

Fig. 1. – Abdominal wall of mouse has been reflected, exposing abdominal viscera. Thoracic cavity has been opened and sternum reflected, exposing thoracic viscera. Organs are *in situ.*

Fig. 2. – Thymic lymphoma. Large, white, anterior mediastinal mass (T) has displaced heart and lungs posteriorly. Leukemia is confined to thoracic cavity. This case was considered to be a nongeneralized thymic lymphoma. Leukemia involves pericardium and pleura.

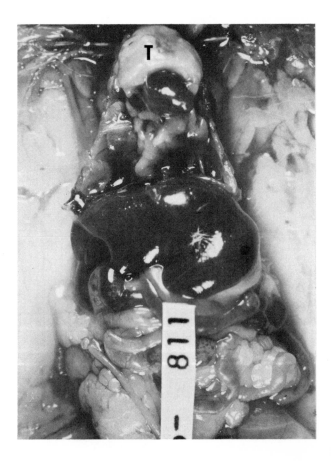

**Fig. 3.** – Leukemic thymus (T) engulfs heart (H) and conforms to pressure of rib cage. H & E. 10×.

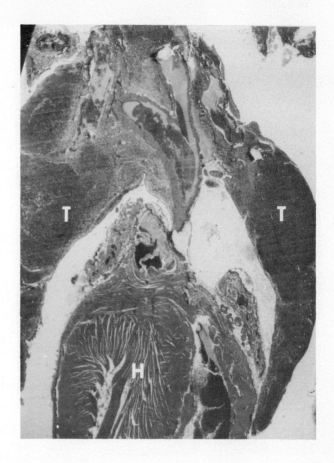

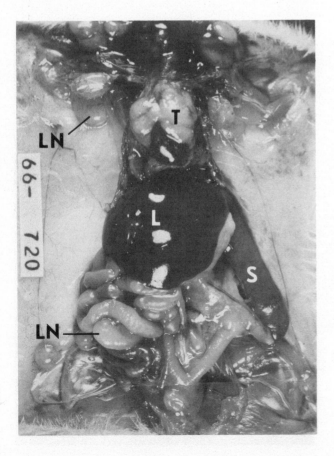

**Fig. 4.** – Thymic lymphoma, generalized. Large, anterior mediastinal mass, thymus (T); liver (L), spleen (S), and lymph nodes (LN) are enlarged and contain leukemic cells. Spleen and liver are smooth and moderately enlarged.

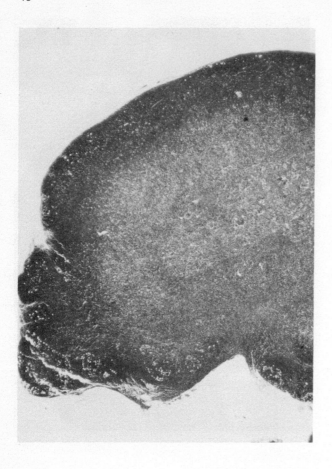

Fig. 5. – Thymic lymphoma in the thymus; architecture almost totally destroyed. Hassall's corpuscles are no longer evident. Homogeneous mass of leukemic cells is seen throughout the thymus. H & E. 15×.

Fig. 6. – Leukemic cells (L) infiltrating myocardium. H & E. 100×.

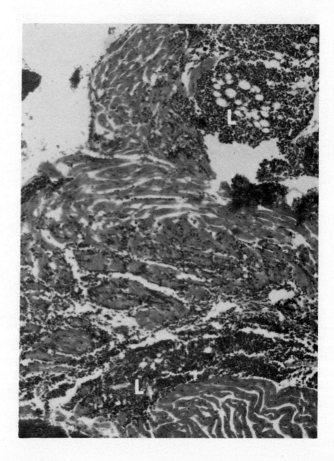

Fig. 7. – Thymic lymphoma (L) invading the pericardium. The infiltration appears as a cheesy, white material on the surface of the heart (H). H & E. 63×.

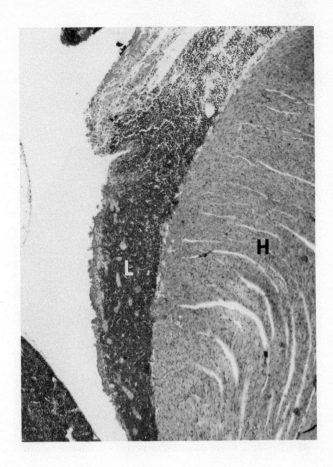

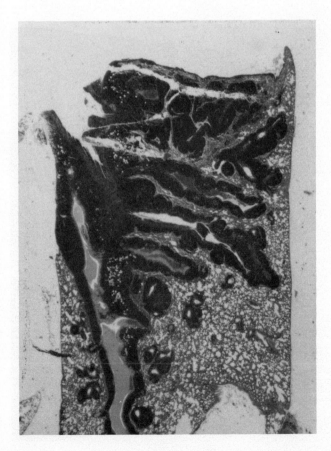

Fig. 8. – Thymic lymphoma in the lungs. Leukemic cells follow the bronchial and vascular tree and present a "cuffed" appearance in pulmonary tissue. H & E. 15×.

Fig. 9. – Thymic lymphoma, generalized, in the liver. Leukemic cells (L) infiltrate perivascularly, especially in portal triads. Fatty infiltration of parenchymal cells is commonly observed. H & E. 25×.

Fig. 10. – Thymic lymphoma (L) infiltrating the spleen. Initial concentrations of leukemic cells occur in red pulp. Lymphatic nodules (N) in germinal centers are still evident. H & E. 63×.

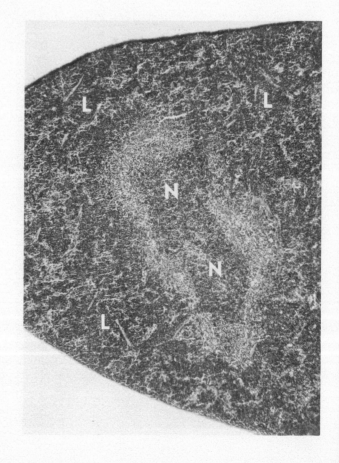

Fig. 11. – Thymic lymphoma in the spleen. There was an extensive infiltration of leukemic cells which destroyed the splenic architecture. Lymphatic nodules are no longer seen. This was considered to be a slower-developing leukemia. H & E. 25×.

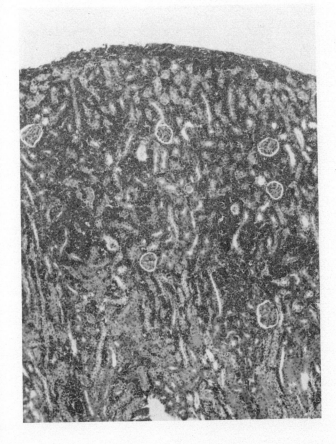

Fig. 12. – Thymic lymphoma infiltrating kidney. Leukemic cell infiltration is extensive, involving subcapsular and inter-tubular tissues. Glomeruli are involved only secondarily. H & E. 80×.

22

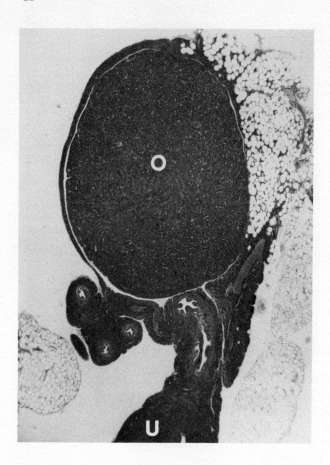

Fig. 13. — Thymic lymphoma, generalized, infiltrating ovary (O) and uterus (U) and associated structures. The ovary was a common site of infiltration, frequently leading to a false impression of ovarian tumors. The ovarian capsule is infiltrated, as are the Fallopian tubes, uterus, and supportive structures. H & E 25×.

Fig. 14. — Thymic lymphoma, generalized. Most tissues, including all lymph nodes (LN), were infiltrated and normal architecture was replaced with leukemic cell masses. H & E. 100×.

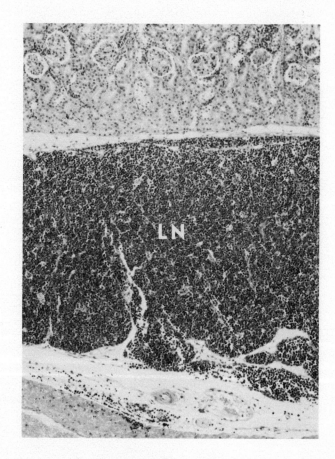

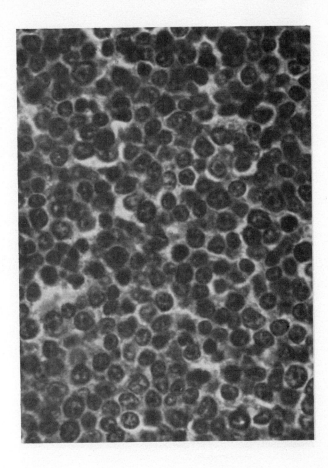

Fig. 15. – Thymic lymphoma in the thymus. Leukemic cells resemble immature lymphocytes, uniform in size and with a large nucleolus and a minimum of cytoplasm which is a typical pale blue. These cells are characteristic of thymic lymphomas, regardless of the extent of organ involvement. H & E. 1000× (oil).

Fig. 16. – Myeloid leukemia. Splenomegaly, hepatomegaly, enlarged lymph nodes, petechiae in the lungs, and bone marrow necrosis in the sternum are shown. Note the smoothness of the liver and spleen and the lack of nodularity. Lymph nodes are green in color; this particular leukemia was designated a chloromyeloid leukemia.

Fig. 17. — Myeloid leukemia in the spleen. This leukemia began in the red pulp and finally obliterated the normal architecture of the spleen. Lymphatic nodules are not easily detected, although some lymphoid cells are present. Megakaryocytes and erythrocytes are also present. H & E. 25×.

Fig. 18. — Myeloid leukemia in the spleen, higher magnification of Fig. 17. Normal architecture has been replaced by leukemic cells. Megakaryocytes (arrows) and erythropoiesis (E) are evident, while lymphatic nodules are not. H & E. 100×.

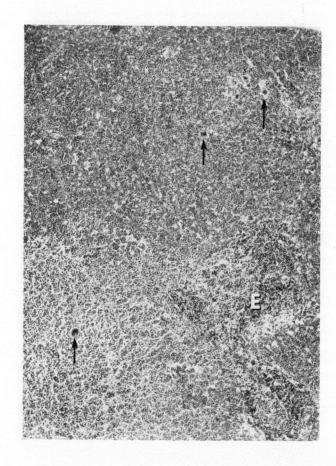

Fig. 19. – Myeloid leukemia in the spleen, higher magnification of Figs 17 and 18. Predominant cell types are of granulocytic series; erythropoiesis (E) is evident. H & E. 560×.

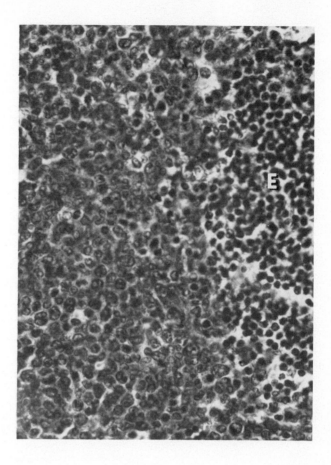

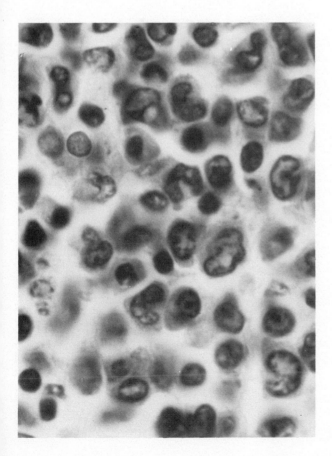

Fig. 20. – Myeloid leukemia in the spleen, higher magnification of Figs 17, 18, and 19. Any stage of the granulocytic series could become leukemic but the cell type most often identified was a metamyelocyte. Nuclei were indented rather than being lobulated or of a doughnut shape. H & E. 1000× (oil).

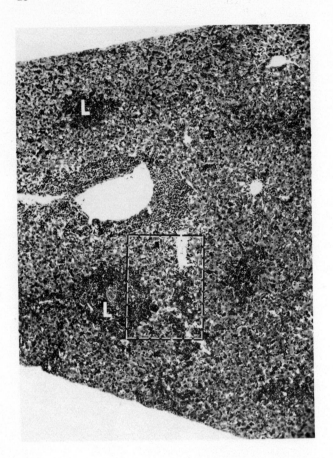

Fig. 21. – Myeloid leukemia in the liver. Leukemic cells (L) are concentrated in the portal areas but are located diffusely throughout the sinusoidal spaces. H & E. 25×.

Fig. 22. – Myeloid leukemia, higher magnification of Fig. 21. Leukemia cells are located diffusely throughout the sinusoidal spaces of the liver, with concentrations in the portal triad areas, and also appear in the blood stream. H & E. 250×.

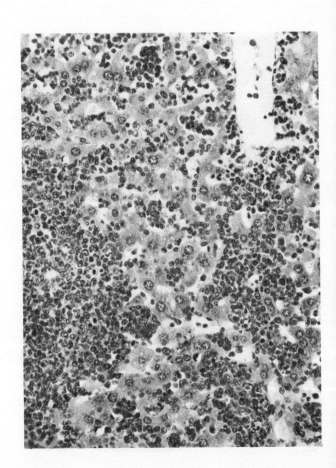

Fig. 23. — Myeloid leukemia in the adrenal gland. Leukemic cells (L) are commonly found in the cortex of the adrenal. H & E. 65×.

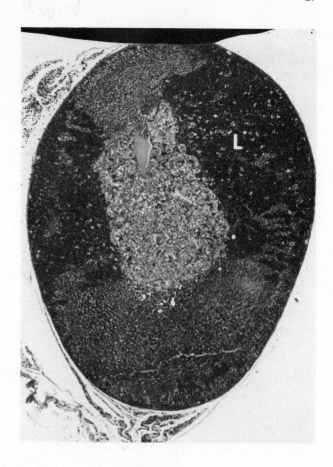

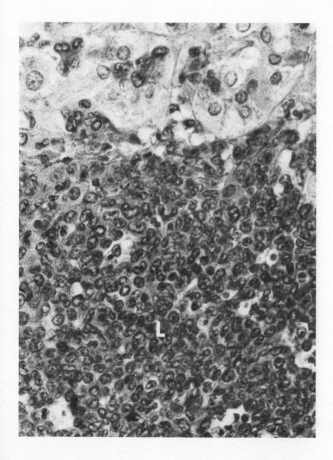

Fig. 24. — Myeloid leukemia, higher magnification of Fig. 23. Leukemic cells (L) are seen in the cortex and extend into the medullary area. H & E. 400×.

28

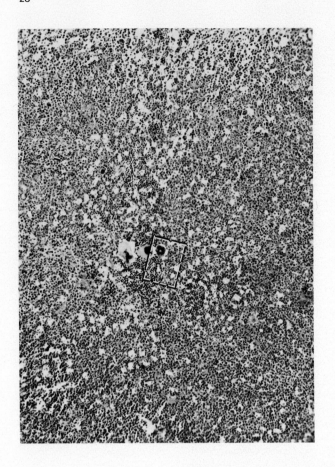

Fig. 25. – Myeloid leukemia in the spleen. Leukemic cells are the dominant cell types in the spleen, but normal cellular elements are also present. H & E. 100×.

Fig. 26. – Myeloid leukemia in the spleen. Higher magnification shows concurrent normal and leukemic elements. Megakaryocytes (M), erythropoiesis (E), and granulocytes of different maturations (G) are evident. H & E. 1000× (oil).

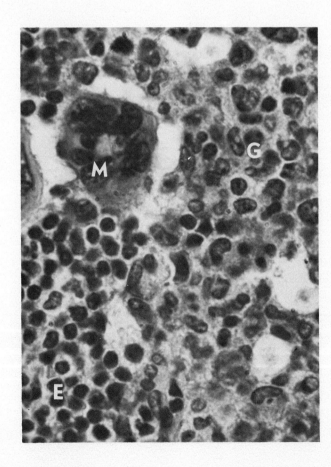

Fig. 27. – Myeloid leukemia in the aorta (A). Massive numbers of leukemic cells (L) are seen in the vessels and heart and are a common finding in myeloid leukemia. H & E. 140×.

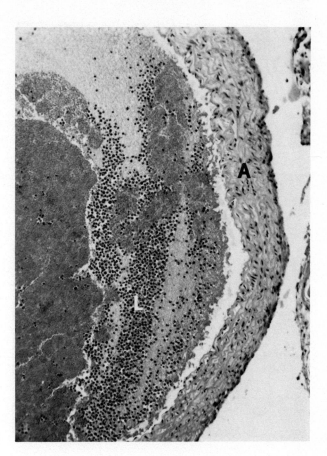

Fig. 28. – Myeloid leukemia in the lung. Leukemic cells form emboli (E – arrows) which occlude smaller arterioles and capillaries within lung parenchyma. These result in the petechiae evident at gross examination. H & E. 100×.

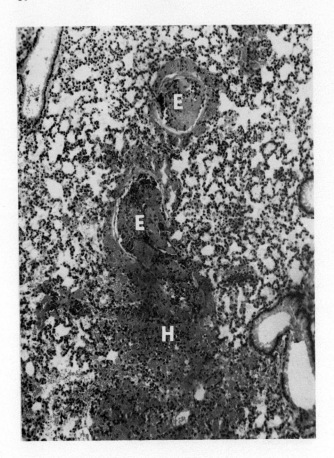

Fig. 29. – Myeloid luekemia in the lung. Emboli (E) of leukemic cells associated with hemorrhage (H) into the lung parenchyma. H & E. 100×.

Fig. 30. – Myeloid leukemia, sternum. Leukemic cells (L) in one compartment of the sternebra and severe necrosis (N) of an adjoining compartment are apparent. This accounts for the differences in compartment cellularity observed in myeloid leukemia upon gross observation. Necrosis of the endochondral junctions are also somewhat evident. H & E. 63×.

**Fig. 31.** – Reticulum cell sarcoma, generalized; hepato-megaly (H) and splenomegaly (S); enlargement of all superficial and deep lymph nodes (L). Note the nodularity of the spleen and liver in contrast to the smooth appearance and homogeneous color of thymic lymphoma (Figs 2, 4) and myeloid leukemia (Fig. 16).

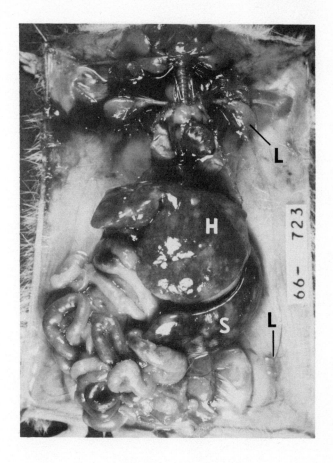

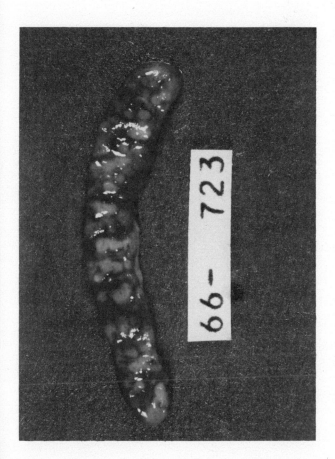

**Fig. 32.** – Spleen from mouse in Fig. 31. Section cut longitudinally through the hilus. Note nodularity and multi-centric involvement of most of the white pulp of the spleen. Contrast this with the smooth, red pulp proliferation (or infiltration) of myeloid leukemia (Fig. 17) and thymic lymphoma (Fig. 10), respectively.

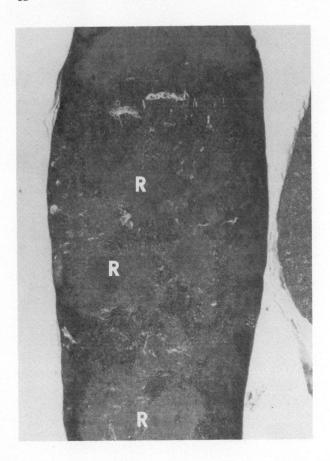

Fig. 33. – Reticulum cell sarcoma in the spleen, same as Fig. 32. Proliferation of reticulum cells (R) within the white pulp, exerting pressure on the red pulp. The process resembles inflation of a balloon in a confined area. H & E. 10×.

Fig. 34. – Reticulum cell sarcoma in the spleen, higher magnification of Fig. 33. Proliferation of reticular cells (R) is accompanied by concurrent erythropoiesis (E) and mega-karyocytopoiesis (M) in the red pulp. H & E. 100×.

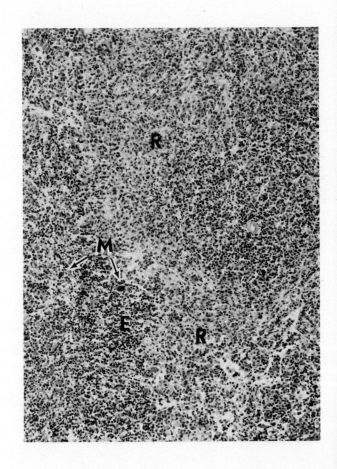

**Fig. 35.** — Same as Fig. 34, reticulum cell proliferation in the splenic white pulp. Pleomorphism of cell type is seen. Some large cells with abundant cytoplasm and large pale reticular nuclei and numerous others with abundant cytoplasm and very small darker-staining nuclei are admixed together. Erythropoiesis is evident. H & E. 250× and 1000× (oil).

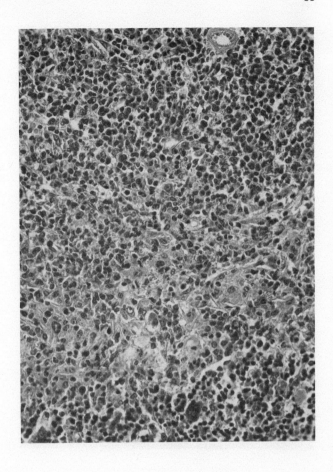

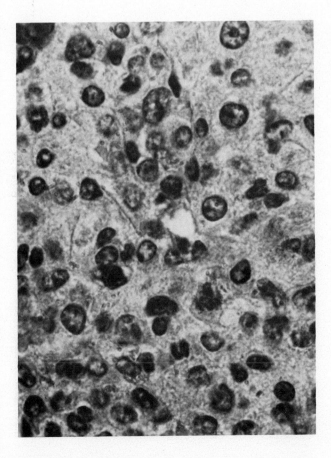

**Fig. 36.** — Same as Fig. 34, reticulum cell proliferation in the splenic white pulp. Pleomorphism of cell type is seen. Some large cells with abundant cytoplasm and large pale reticular nuclei and numerous others with abundant cytoplasm and very small darker-staining nuclei are admixed together. Erythropoiesis is evident. H & E. 250× and 1000× (oil).

**Fig. 37.** – Reticulum cell sarcoma in the liver. Nodular and indiscrete distribution of leukemia cells (L) throughout liver parenchyma (P). H & E. 25×.

**Fig. 38.** – Reticulum cell sarcoma, higher magnification of Fig. 37. Nodular growth of reticular cells occurs within the liver, causing pressure necrosis and replacement of the parenchymal cells. H & E. 63×.

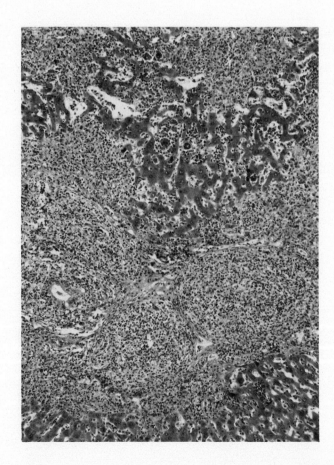

Fig. 39. — Reticulum cell sarcoma, abdominal; enlarged mesentery lymph node (N) and Peyer's patches. Spleen and liver are normal but may also be involved in other cases.

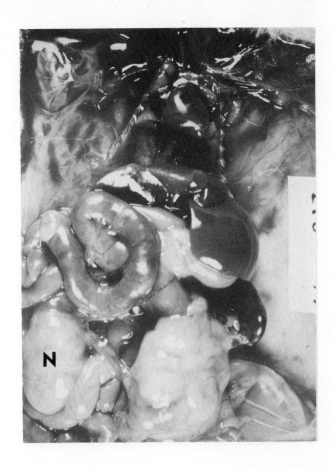

**1822841**

Fig. 40. — Reticulum cell, abdominal. The mesenteric lymph node is markedly enlarged. Infarcted area (I) and proliferation of reticular cells are shown. Some nodal structures are still evident. H & E. 10×.

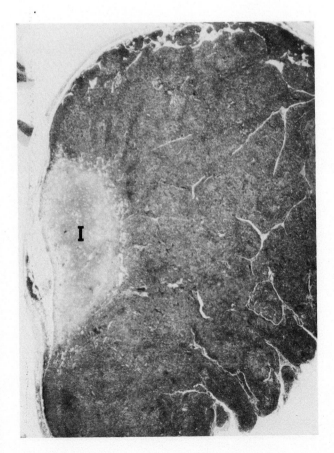

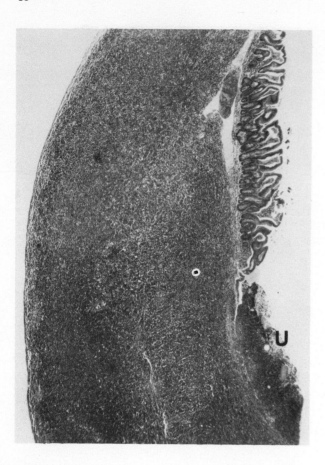

Fig. 41. – Reticulum cell sarcoma, abdominal; Peyer's patch in small intestine, with proliferation of reticular cells. Ulceration (U) of the intestinal mucosa is seen. H & E. 25×.

Fig. 42. – Reticulum cell sarcoma (R) in the liver. There is a pronounced nodular arrangement of leukemic cells. H & E. 63×.

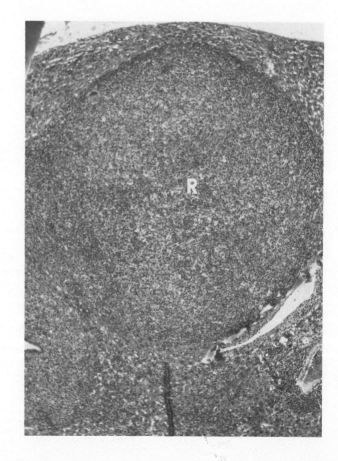

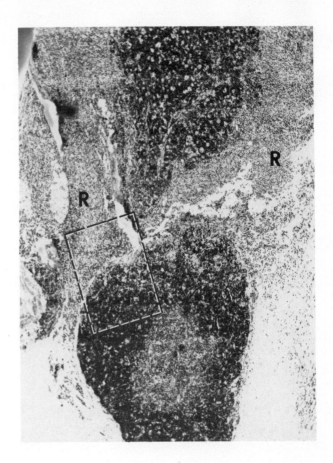

**Fig. 43.** – Reticulum cell sarcoma, generalized. Leukemic cells (R) have secondarily invaded the thymus and cortical atrophy is evident. H & E. 63×.

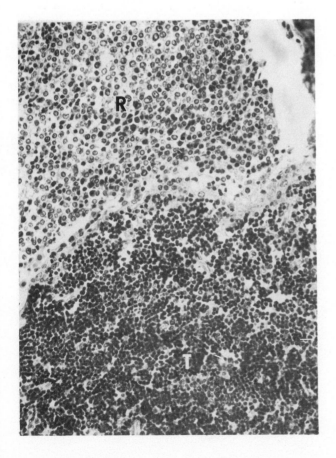

**Fig. 44.** – Reticulum cell sarcoma, higher magnification of Fig. 43. Reticular cell hyperplasia (R) has infiltrated the thymus (T) and other mediastinal structures. H & E. 250×.

38

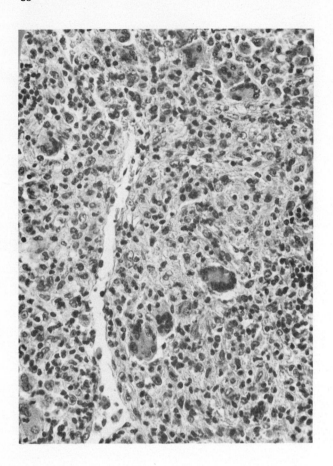

Fig. 45. – Reticulum cell sarcoma, lymph node. This variant of the reticulum cell sarcoma contains multiple giant cells with peripheral nuclei and had some resemblance to human Hodgkin's disease. This was not a common manifestation and was called a "Hodgkinoid" variant of reticulum cell sarcoma. H & E. 375×.

Fig. 46. – Nonthymic lymphoma, spleen. Increased lymphoid elements (L) in the white pulp of the spleen appear concurrently with leukemoid reaction (LR) in the red pulp; leukemia originated in the lymphatic nodule. H & E. 25×.

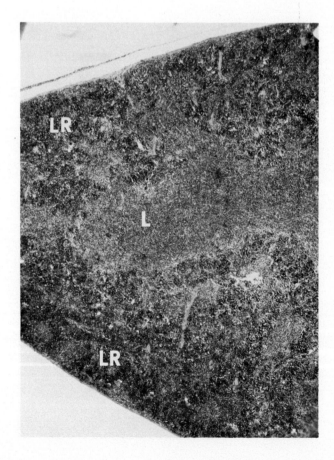

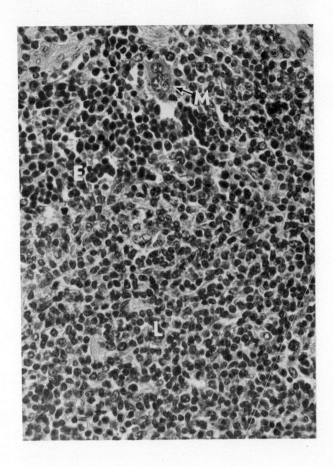

Fig. 47. – Nonthymic lymphoma, same mouse as in Fig. 46. Leukemic cells (L) dominate the lymphatic nodule cell population. Erythropoiesis (E) and megakaryocytopoiesis (M) are both seen in the red pulp. H & E. 400×.

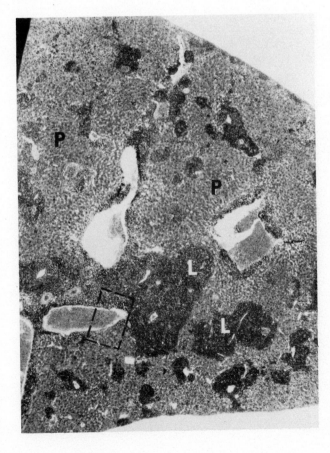

Fig. 48. – Nonthymic lymphoma in the liver of same mouse as Figs. 46 and 47. The perivascular infiltration of leukemic cells (L) within the liver parenchyma (P) resembles distribution of thymic lymphoma. H & E. 32×.

40

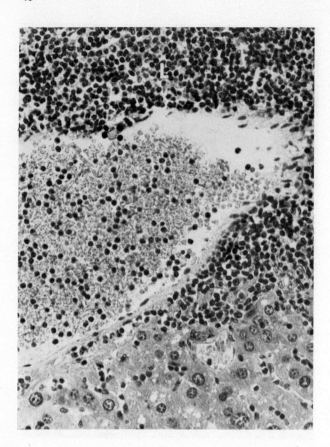

Fig. 49. – Nonthymic lymphoma in the liver, higher magnification of Fig. 48. Leukemic infiltration (L) is located perivascularly and occurs in high concentration in the blood vessels. H & E. 250×.

Fig. 50. – Nonthymic lymphoma, higher magnification of area in Fig. 49 showing perivascular lymphocytic leukemic infiltration. Leukemic cells are mature lymphocytes, and are found in the vessels of the liver and in the sinusoids. Cells are more mature than those usually found in thymic lymphoma. H & E. 800×.

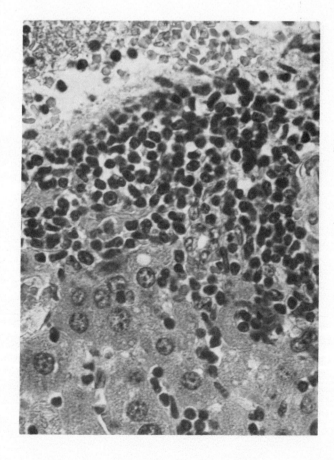

Fig. 51. — Nonthymic lymphoma in the kidney of same animal as in Figs 46–50. Infiltration is primarily perivascular; leukemic cells are seen intravascularly within the kidney. H & E. 400×.

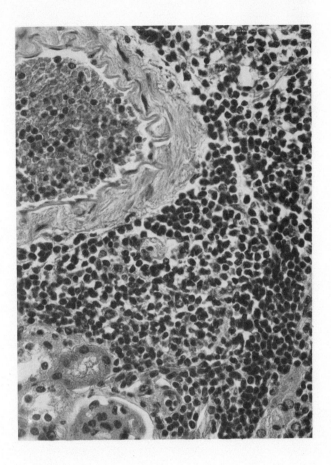

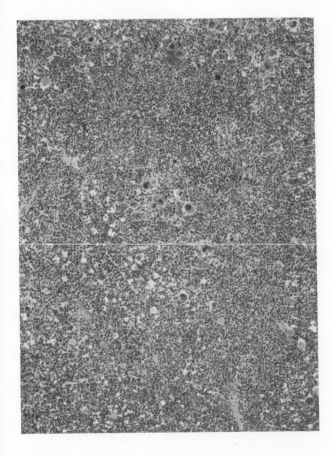

Fig. 52. — Leukemoid reaction in the spleen. Marked hyperplasia of all three cellular elements of the red pulp (granulocytopoiesis, megakaryocytopoiesis, and erythropoiesis) is seen. H & E. 63×.

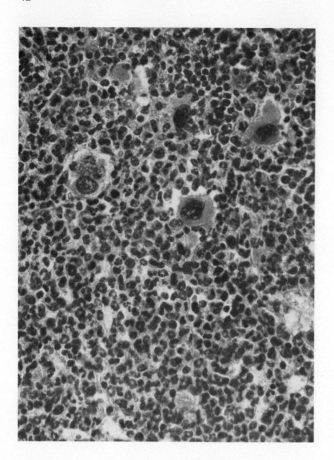

Fig. 53. – Higher magnification of Fig. 52. All three elements of the red pulp are evident. Maturation of the granulocytopoietic series is seen. H & E. 500×.

Fig. 54. – Leukemoid reaction in the liver. Portal triads have marked granulocytopoietic activity, with all forms of maturation evident. H & E. 250×.

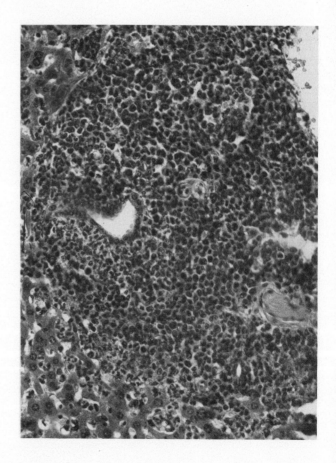

**Fig. 55.** – Pulmonary adenoma. Proliferation of alveolar parenchymal (A) cells usually occurs in the periphery of the lobe. H & E. 150×.

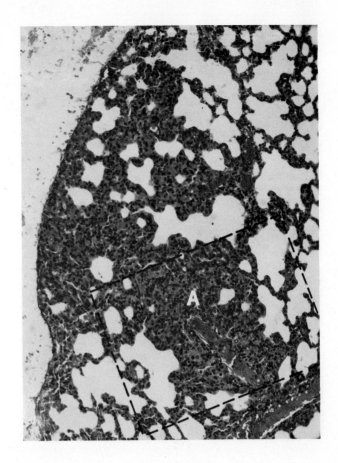

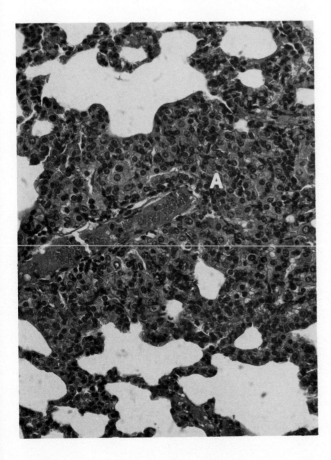

**Fig. 56.** – Pulmonary adenoma. Further magnification of area seen in Fig. 55 shows proliferation of parenchymal cells in early adenoma (A). H & E. 250×.

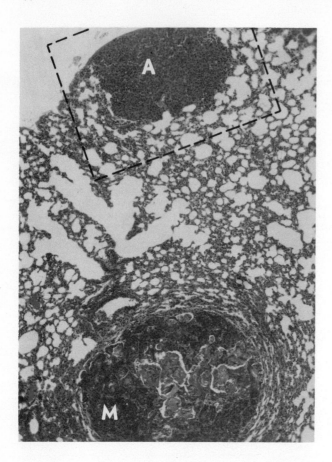

Fig. 57. – Primary pulmonary adenoma in the periphery of the lung (A) and a metastatic tumor (M) from an osteogenic sarcoma. The primary adenoma was visible grossly. H & E. 63×.

Fig. 58. – Pulmonary adenoma, higher magnification of area in Fig. 57. Primary pulmonary adenoma (A) in the periphery of the lung appears as a pearly white nodule. H & E. 100×.

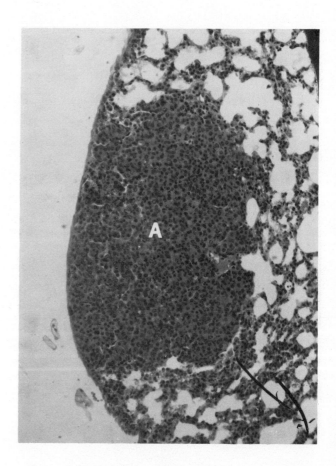

45

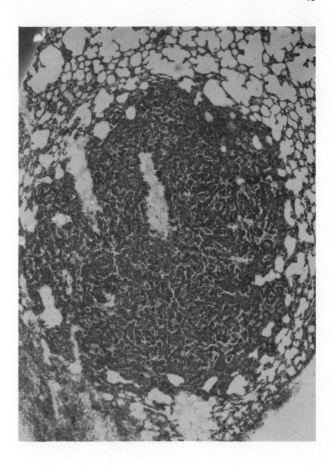

**Fig. 59.** – Pulmonary papillary adenoma, primary. Adenomas became papillary in structure as size increased. H & E. 63×.

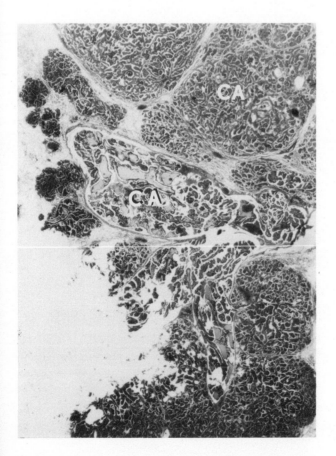

**Fig. 60.** – Pulmonary adenocarcinoma (CA), primary. Tumor has invaded the bronchioles extensively. Metastases were rare. H & E. 20×.

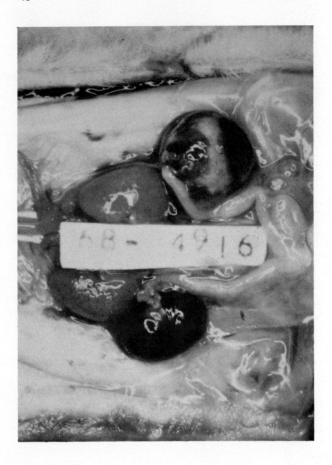

Fig. 61. – Bilateral ovarian tumor. These tumors, similar histologically, were tubular adenomas. A subcapsular hemorrhage of the tumor of the left ovary caused a difference in gross appearance. Glomerulosclerosis is evident in the kidneys and the uterus is hypertrophied.

Fig. 62. – Pretumor of irradiated ovary. Luteal and stromal cells comprise most of the inner portion of the ovary. Tubular epithelial elements compose the outer layers. This is prior to sufficient proliferation of the elements to become a benign tumor. H & E. 63X.

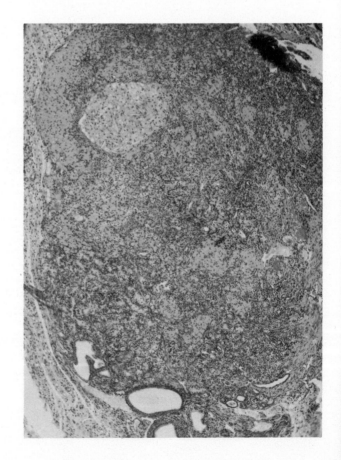

**Fig. 63.** – Ovarian tumor of the left ovary shown in Fig. 61. Tumor is a tubular adenoma with subcapsular hemorrhage. H & E. 10×.

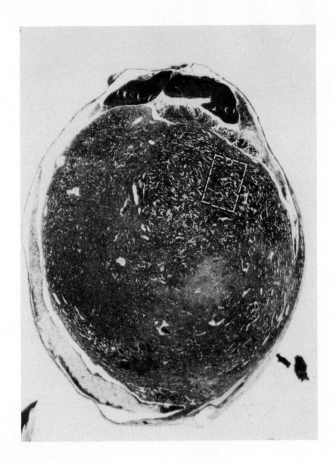

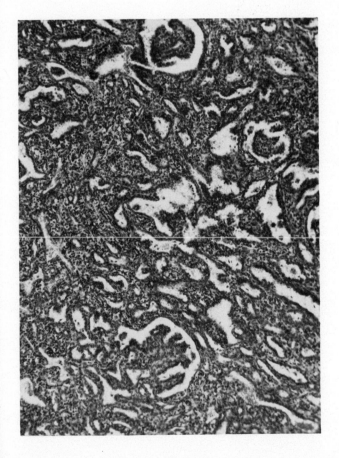

**Fig. 64.** – Ovarian tumor, further magnification of area shown in Fig. 63. The predominant manifestation is tubular adenoma, with occasional papillary formations. H & E. 100×.

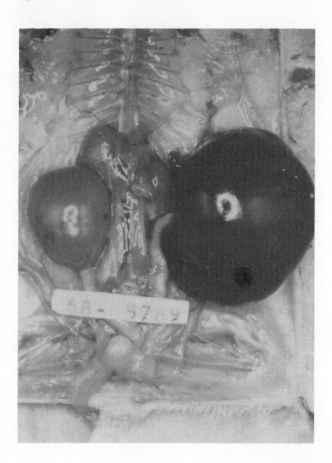

Fig. 65. – Bilateral ovarian tumor with hemorrhagic cyst of right ovary.

Fig. 66. – Ovarian tumor with hemorrhagic cyst (H) from Fig. 65. Tumor (T) is quite small as compared with gross observation. H & E. 20×.

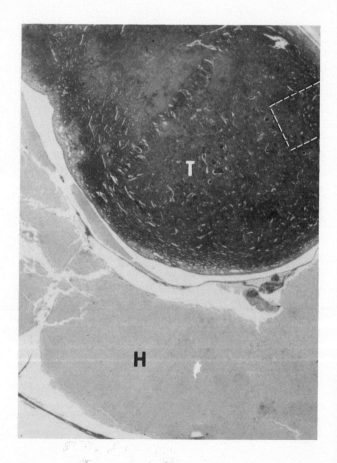

49

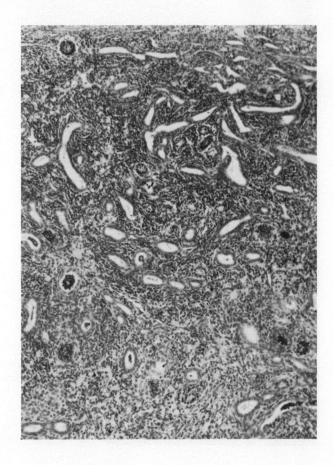

Fig. 67. – Further magnification of ovarian tumor in Fig. 66. Proliferation of tubular and stromal elements is shown. H & E. 120×.

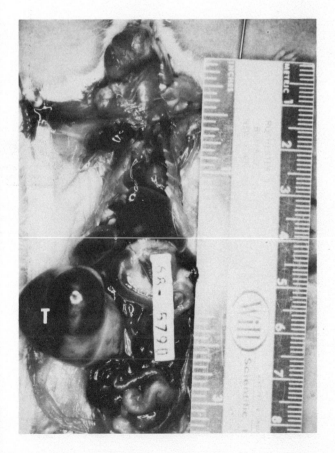

Fig. 68. – Ovarian tumor (T), lobulated, 22 mm.

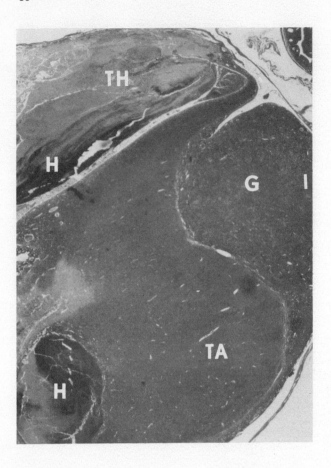

**Fig. 69.** – Ovarian tumor shown grossly in Fig. 68. Multiple cellular elements comprise the nodules of the tumor. Granulosa cell (G) and tubular adenoma (TA) components with focal areas of hemorrhage (H) are shown and thrombi (TH) are also seen. H & E. 10×.

**Fig. 70.** – Further magnification of ovarian tumor shown in Figs. 68 and 69. A sharp demarcation is evident in the marginal area between granulosa cell elements (G) and tubular adenoma elements (TA). H & E. 200×.

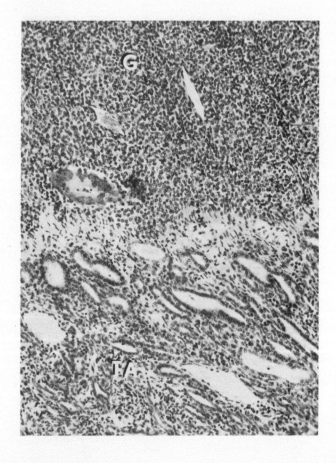

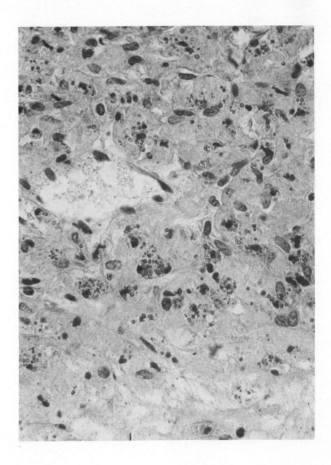

Fig. 71. – Same ovarian tumor as in Figs 68–70. Granulosa cell elements of solid tumor with macrophage cells containing hemosiderin are shown. Granulosa elements are not forming pseudofollicles in this tumor. H & E. 500×.

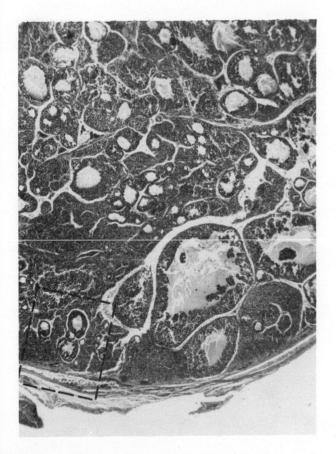

Fig. 72. – Ovarian tumor, granulosa cell. Tumor cells are attempting to form bizarre follicles. H & E. 50×.

52

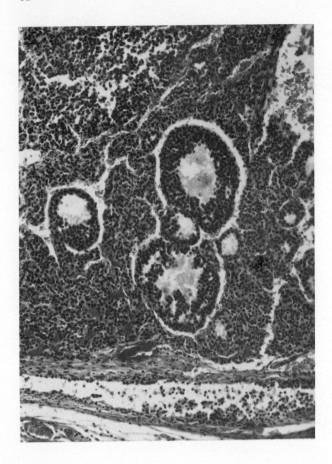

Fig. 73. – Ovarian tumor, granulosa cell tumor, magnification of area seen in Fig. 72. Follicle formation of tumor cells is evident, while other tumor cells are forming undifferentiated foci. H & E. 150×.

Fig. 74. – Ovarian tumor, granulosa cell (G), papillary adenoma (PA), tubular adenoma (TA). Tumor nodules tend to be discrete, with each cell type forming an individual nodule. H & E. 25×.

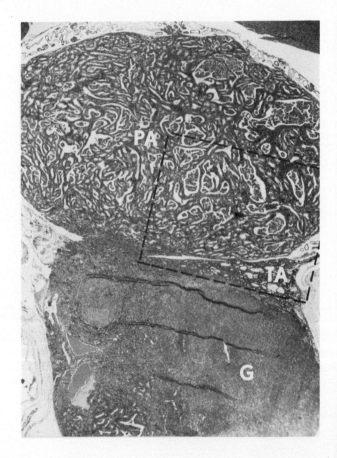

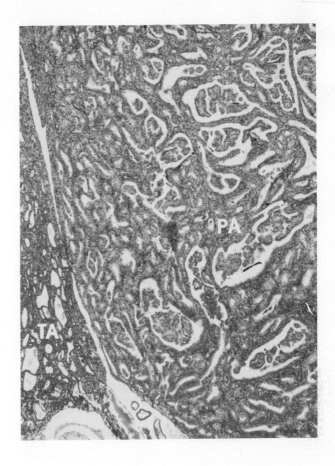

Fig. 75. – Ovarian tumor, magnification of area seen in Fig. 74. A distinct margin between tubular adenoma elements (TA) and papillary adenomas (PA) is evident within the tumor. H & E. 63×.

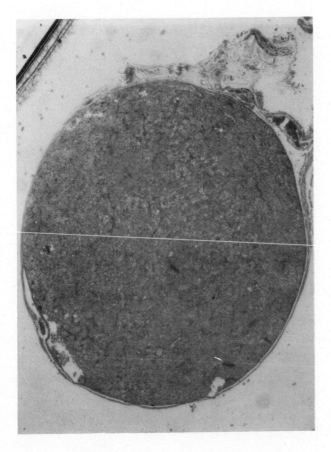

Fig. 76. – Ovarian tumor, luteoma. Mass is composed entirely of luteal cells and supportive structures. H & E. 20×.

54

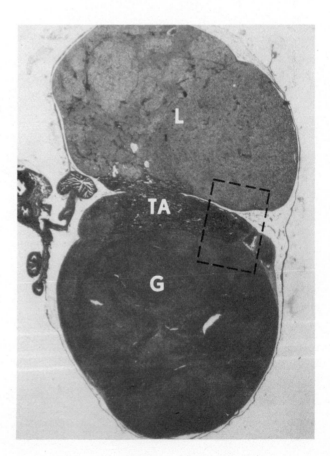

**Fig. 77.** – Ovarian tumor, luteoma, higher magnification of Fig. 76. Cells are very large with abundant cytoplasm; lipid-like vacuoles appear within the cytoplasm of many cells. H & E. 200×.

**Fig. 78.** – Ovarian tumor; granulosa cell luteoma (G), luteoma (L), and tubular adenoma (TA). Distinct nodules of each tumor element are evident. H & E. 15×.

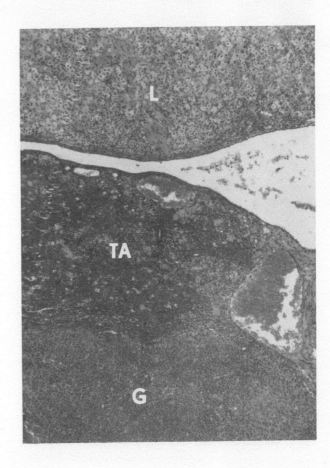

Fig. 79. – Magnification of ovarian tumor in Fig. 78. Granulosa elements (G) are not forming follicles. Tubular adenoma elements (TA) are compressed between two nodules. Luteal cells (L) compose the other aspect of the tumor. H & E. 95×.

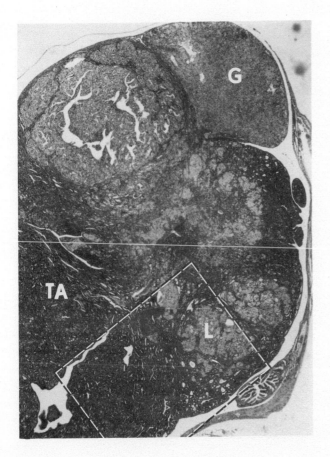

Fig. 80. – Ovarian tumor, granulosa cell (G), luteoma (L) and tubular adenoma (TA). Admixture of components is more pronounced than in Figs 78 and 79. H & E. 25×.

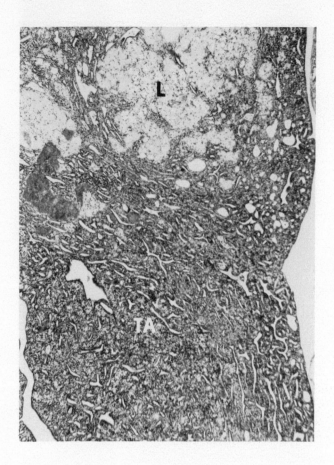

**Fig. 81.** – Section of ovarian tumor magnified from area in Fig. 80. Admixture of luteal (L) and tubular adenoma (TA) elements is seen. H & E. 63×.

**Fig. 82.** – Ovarian tumor. Line of separation between granulosa elements (G) and luteal elements (L) is apparent. H & E. 250×.

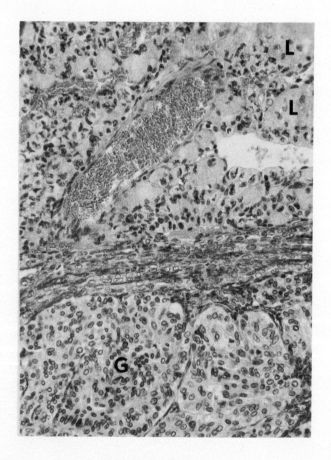

**Fig. 83.** – Ovarian tumor; granulosa cell luteoma, tubular adenoma, and hemangioendotheliomal elements. At this magnification primarily granulosa cell elements may be seen. H & E. 100×.

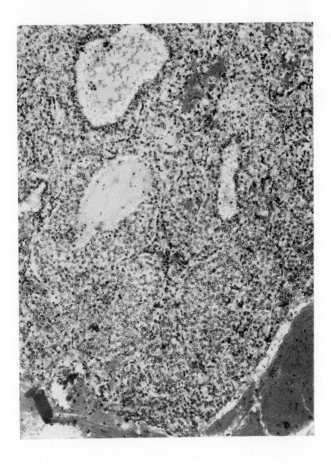

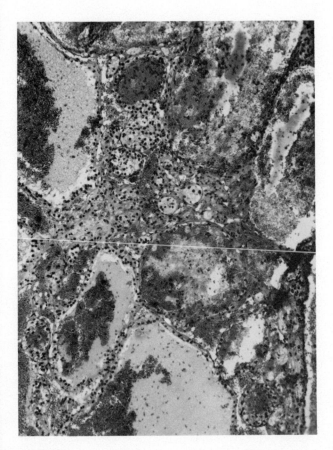

**Fig. 84.** – Ovarian tumor, same as in Fig. 83. Hemangioendotheliomal element of this mixed tumor is dominant. H & E. 100×.

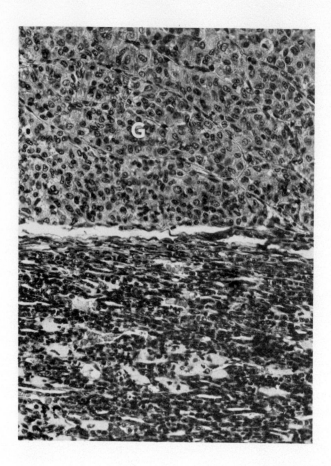

Fig. 85. – Same ovarian tumor as in Figs 83 and 84. Discrete separation between granulosa cell (G) nodule and admixture of luteal and tubular adenomas is apparent. H & E. 250×.

Fig. 86. – Ovarian tumor containing luteal, papillary adenoma, and tubular adenoma elements. H & E. 25×.

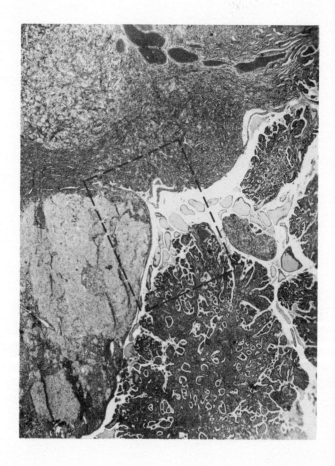

Fig. 87. – Ovarian tumor, higher magnification of area in Fig. 86. Three elements are seen in this enlargement, luteal (L), tubular adenoma (TA), and papillary adenoma (PA). H & E.

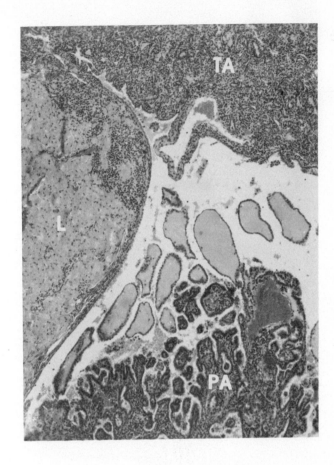

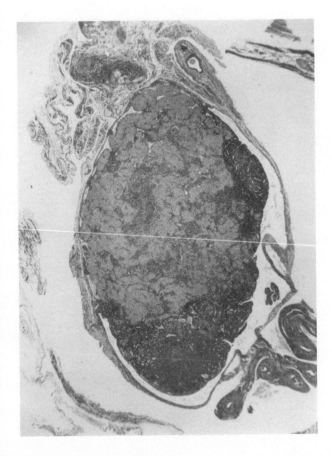

Fig. 88. – Ovarian tumor: luteoma and tubular adenoma. H & E. 25×.

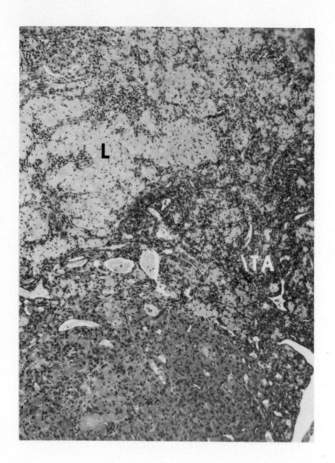

Fig. 89. – Ovarian tumor, as in Fig. 88. Luteal (L) and tubular adenoma (TA) elements are admixed. H & E. 100×.

Fig. 90. – Ovarian tumor, as in Figs 88 and 89. Polyarteritis (P) and hyalinization of arteriole (H) within the luteal elements of the tumor are shown. H & E. 250×.

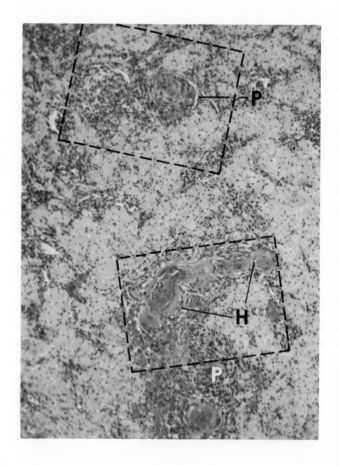

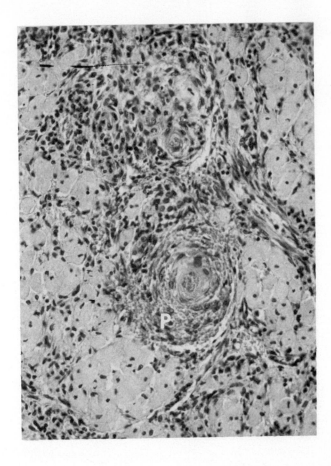

Fig. 91. — Same ovarian tumor as in Figs 88–90, magnification of area indicated (P) in Fig. 90. Polyarteritis (P) involving small arterioles. H & E. 400×.

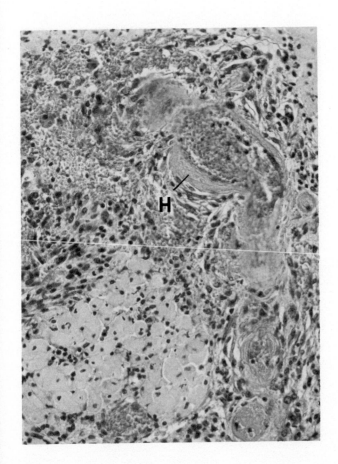

Fig. 92. — Same ovarian tumor as in Figs 88–91, magnification of area indicated (H) in Fig. 90. Hyalin deposits (H) accompany polyarteritic changes in small arterioles within the tumor. H & E. 400×.

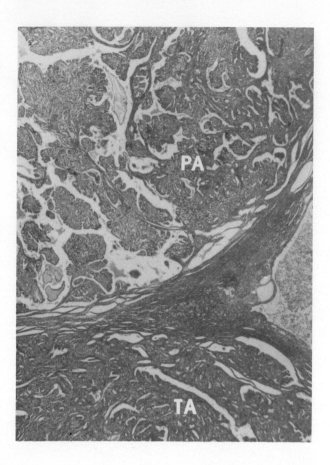

Fig. 93. – Ovarian tumor, papillary adenoma (PA) and tubular adenoma (TA). Distinct nodules of each of the adenomatous elements is evident. H & E. 25×.

Fig. 94. – Ovarian tumor, luteoma and tubular adenoma elements. Cholesterol clefts are seen in the luteal elements of the tumor mass. H & E. 83×.

Fig. 95. – Osteogenic sarcoma, left femur (O). Multiple tumor nodules in lungs.

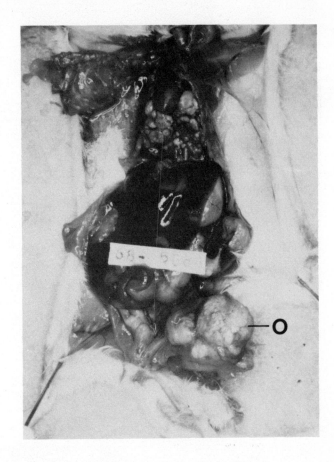

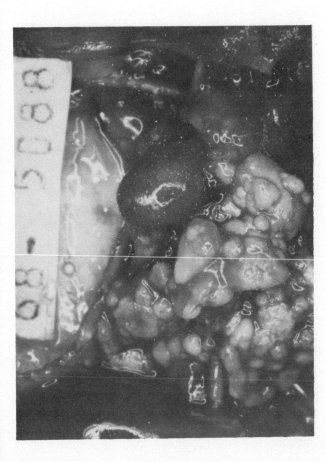

Fig. 96. – Same osteogenic sarcoma as shown in Fig. 95. Multiple metastatic tumor nodules in the lungs from primary osteogenic sarcoma, left femur, are seen.

64

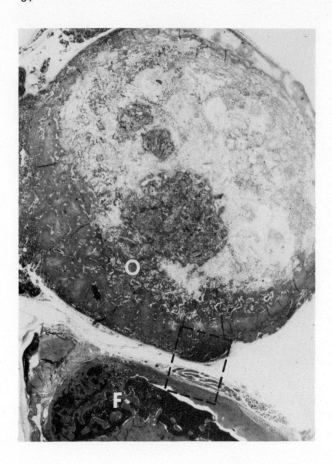

Fig. 97. – Same osteogenic sarcoma as in Figs 95 and 96. Osteogenic sarcoma (O) is associated with left femur (F). H & E. 10X.

Fig. 98. – Same osteogenic sarcoma as in Fig. 97. Tumor with bone formation (O) appears next to femur. H & E. 95X.

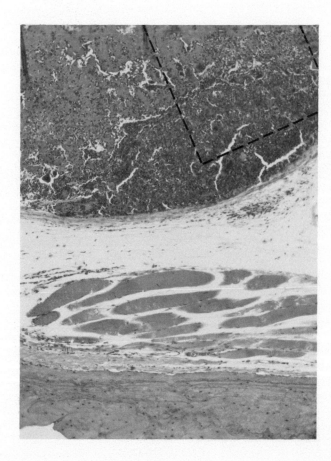

Fig. 99. – Osteogenic sarcoma, higher magnification of area from Fig. 98. Bone formation (B) within tumor. H & E. 200×.

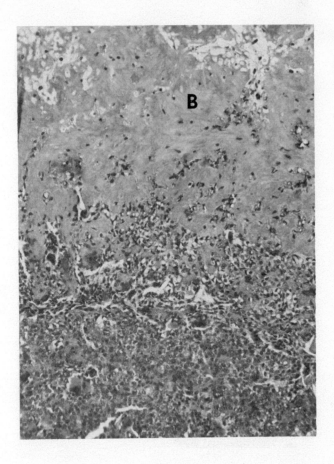

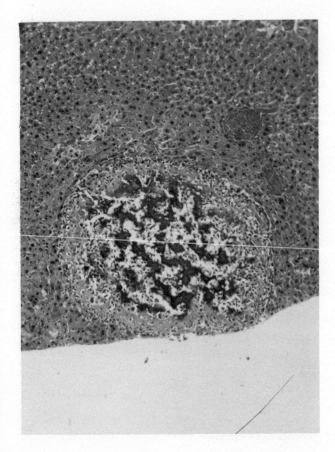

Fig. 100. – Osteogenic sarcoma, metastatic nodule to the liver, from same mouse as in Figs 97–99. Note bone formation in metastasis. H & E. 100×.

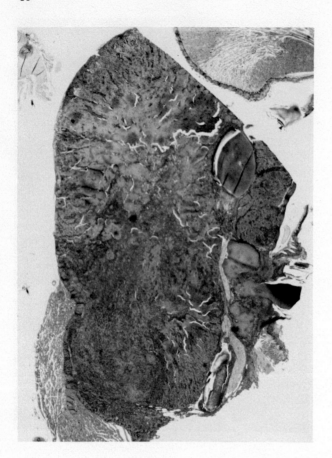

Fig. 101. – Osteogenic sarcoma, right mandible. H & E. 10X.

Fig. 102. – Osteogenic sarcoma, higher magnification of Fig. 101. Proliferation of tumor cells with bone formation is shown. H & E. 95X.

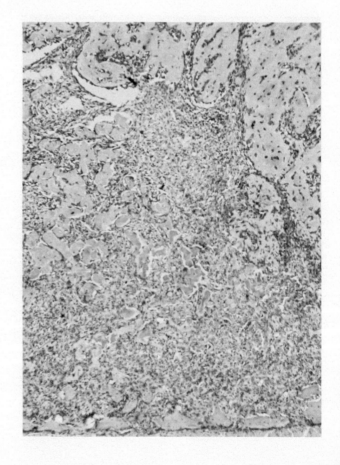

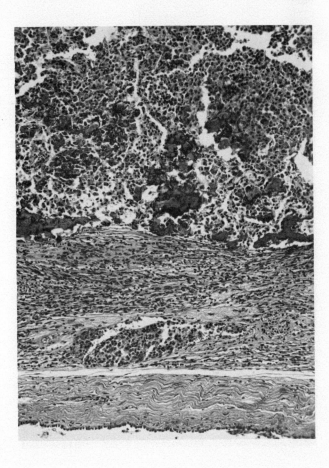

Fig. 103. – Osteogenic sarcoma, primary site considered to be pelvis. Tumor has invaded the supportive tissues and muscle layers. Bone formation is seen in the tumor. H & E. 150×.

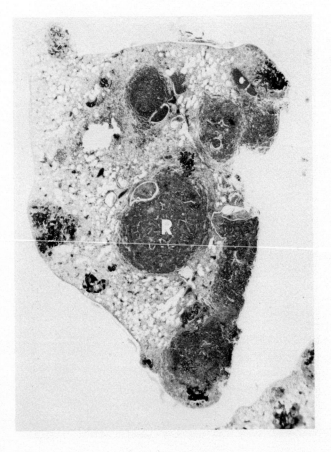

Fig. 104. – Osteogenic sarcoma, metastatic to the lung, same animal as Fig. 103. Multiple tumor nodules with bone formation are seen, as are also some nodules of reticulum cell sarcoma (R) in the lungs. H & E. 10×.

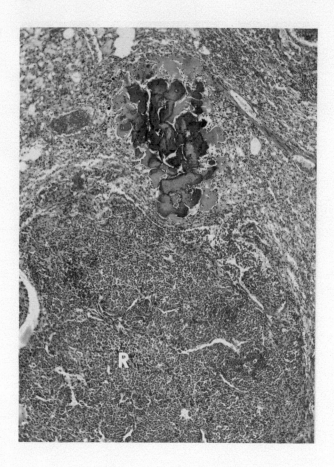

Fig. 105. – Osteogenic sarcoma, metastatic to the lung, same animal as Fig. 103. Multiple tumor nodules with bone formation are seen, as are also some nodules of reticulum cell sarcoma (R) in the lungs. H & E. 10×.

Fig. 106. – Osteogenic sarcoma, metastatic to liver, same animal as Figs 103–105. Bone formation is seen in metastasis. H & E. 100×.

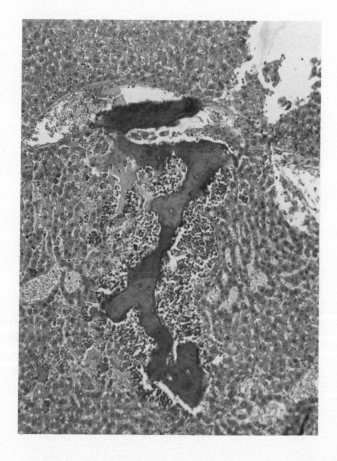

Fig. 107. – Osteogenic sarcoma (O), same animal as in Figs. 103–106. Tumor embolus is seen in the right ventricle of the heart. H & E. 200×.

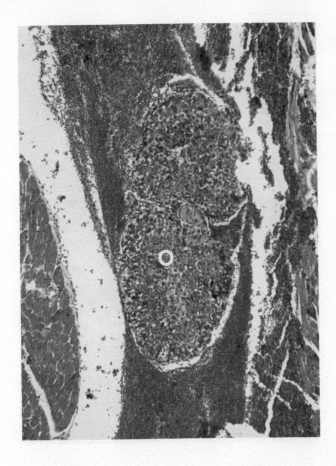

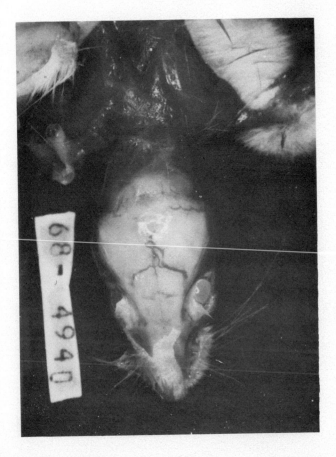

Fig. 108. – Pituitary gland tumor with bulging of cranium. Note enlarged cranial vessels with skin reflected off the cranium.

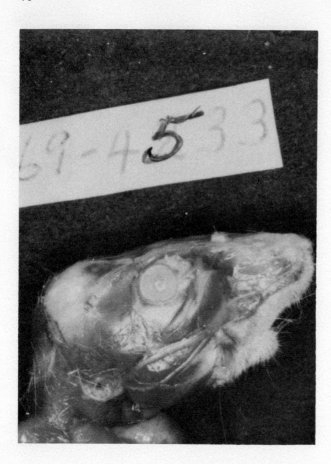

Fig. 109. – Pituitary gland tumor. Note elevated frontal and parietal bones of skull, a rather consistent and presumptive external evidence of a pituitary gland tumor.

Fig. 110. – Pituitary gland tumor, same one as shown in Fig. 108. Cranium has been removed and the brain reflected posteriorly to reveal pituitary gland tumor. Tumor is hemorrhagic.

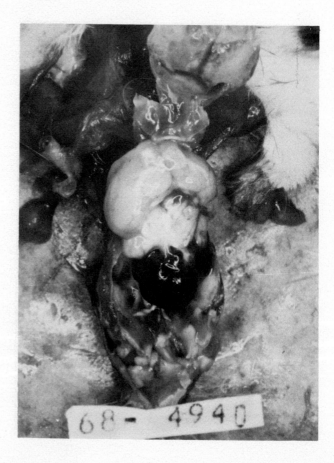

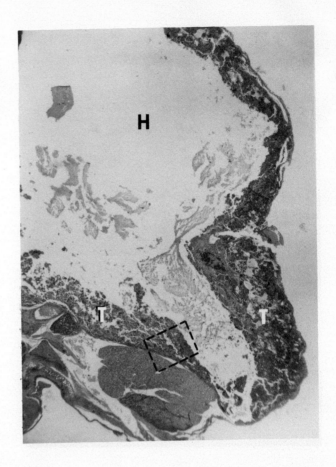

**Fig. 111.** – Same pituitary gland tumor as in Figs 108 and 110. Hemorrhagic area (H) has been lost by processing. Tumor cells (T) line the exterior portion of the tumor. H & E. 25×.

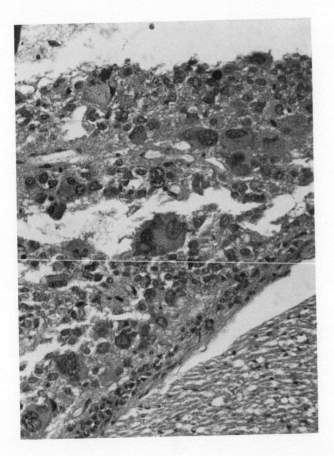

**Fig. 112.** – Pituitary gland tumor, higher magnification of area indicated on Fig. 111. Solid portion of tumor exhibits pleomorphism; numerous giant cells and cellular atypia are seen. H & E. 250×.

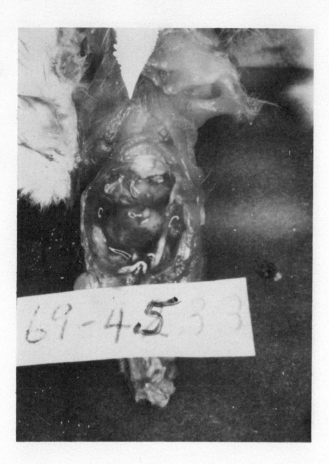

Fig. 113. – Same pituitary gland tumor as in Fig. 109. Brain has been removed to reveal solid pituitary tumor.

Fig. 114. – Pituitary gland tumor in Figs 109 and 113 as seen histologically. Tumor is solid; some cystic and hemorrhagic areas are seen. H & E. 25×.

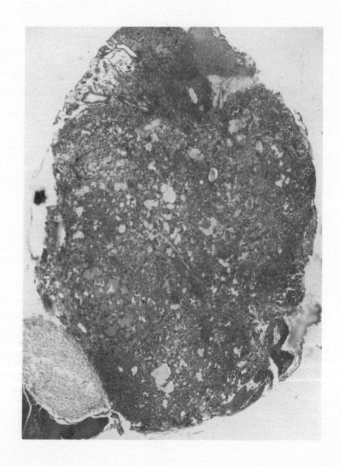

Fig. 115. – Same pituitary gland tumor as in Fig. 114. Dominant cell is small with round nucleus and moderate cytoplasm but some cellular atypia and giant cells are present. Predominant cell is negative for granule staining. H & E. 250×.

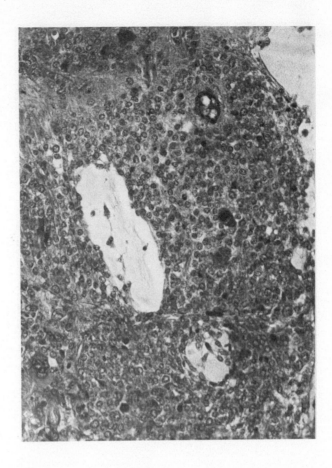

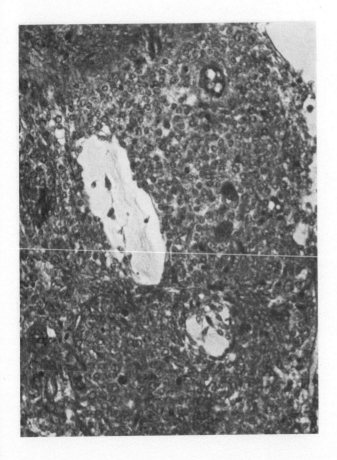

Fig. 116. – Same pituitary gland tumor as in Fig. 114. Staining is Gude's modification of Martin-Mallory (GMM) technique for granule staining of pituitary cells. Cells are negative for granule staining, as was typical in most pituitary tumors, and diagnosis of chromophobe adenomas resulted. 250×.

74

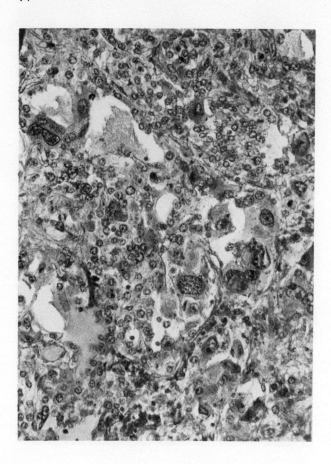

Fig. 117. – Same pituitary gland tumor as in Fig. 114, chromophobe adenoma. Chromophobe cells are dominant, with giant cells and cellular atypia common. H & E. 250×.

Fig. 118. – Mammary gland tumor, right inguinal area. Skin is reflected to show extent of tumor invasiveness.

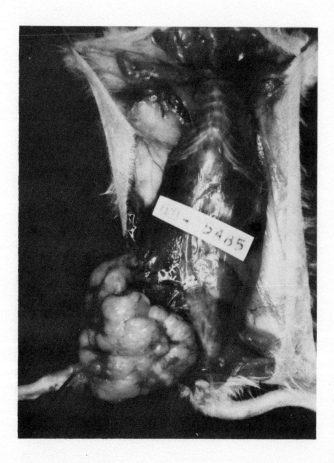

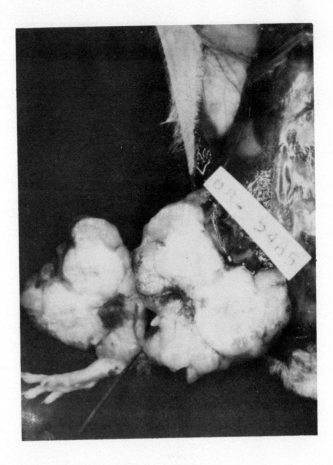

**Fig. 119.** – Same mammary gland tumor as seen in Fig. 118. Tumor has been sectioned; firm nodular mass was white and of cheesy consistency on cut surface. Large necrotic areas are also seen in the tumor.

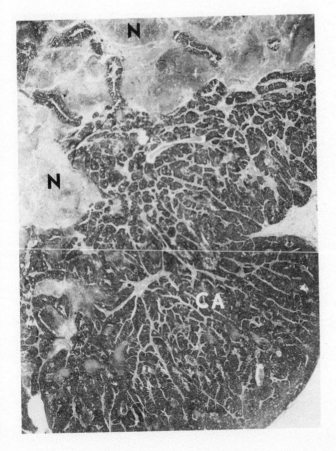

**Fig. 120.** – Mammary gland adenocarcinoma (CA) shown in Figs 118 and 119 as seen histologically. Necrotic (N) areas are also evident. H & E. 25×.

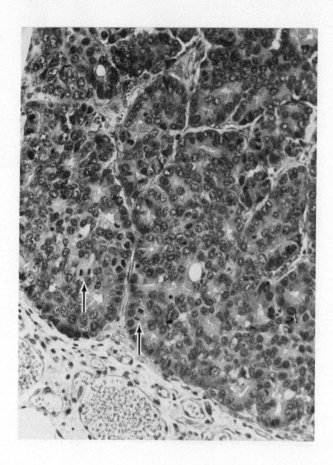

Fig. 121. – Same mammary gland adenocarcinoma as in Fig. 120. Cells are arranged in a glandular formation. Numerous mitotic figures (arrows) are seen. Tumor was moderately invasive. H & E. 250×.

Fig. 122. – Mammary gland adenocarcinoma, metastatic to lung. Multiple tumor nodules are seen in the lungs. Tumor cells very closely resemble primary tumor in Figs 120 and 121. H & E. 10×.

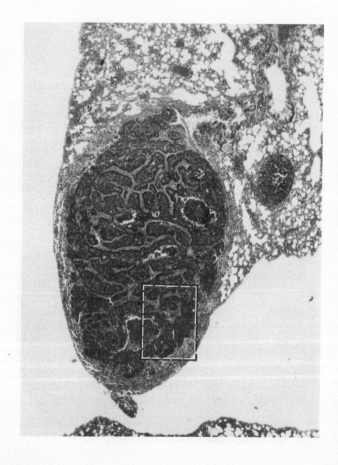

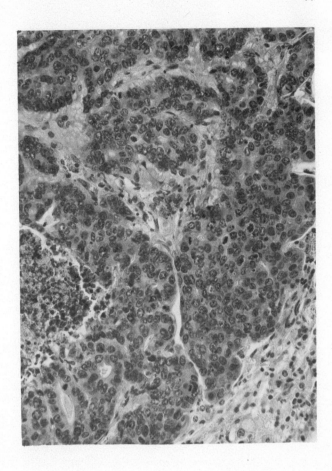

Fig. 123. – Same mammary adenocarcinoma, metastatic to the lung, as in Fig. 122. Tumor cells form glandular structures; numerous mitotic cells are seen and necrosis is evident. H & E. 250×.

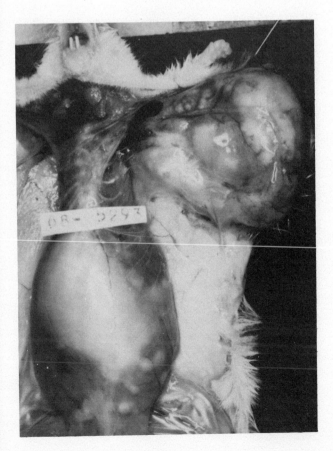

Fig. 124. – Mammary gland tumor, with skin reflected exposing tumor mass *in situ*. Subcutaneous mass is primarily located outside the thoracic cavity.

78

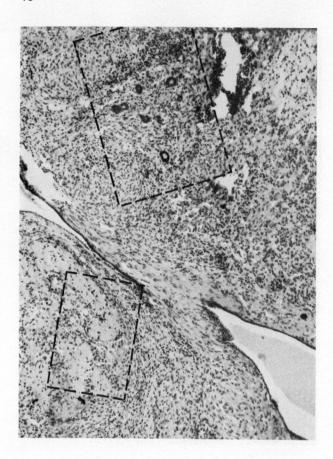

Fig. 125. – Magnified mammary gland tumor shown in Fig. 124. Tumor mass was predominantly fibrous, with whorled formations and numerous mitotically active cells. Occasional tubular formations were seen. H & E. 100×.

Fig. 126. – Mammary adenofibrosarcoma of left axillary region shown in Fig. 125. Dominant cell was fibroblastic in nature, with a whorl pattern. H & E. 100×.

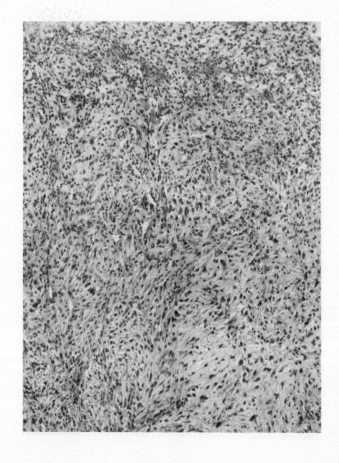

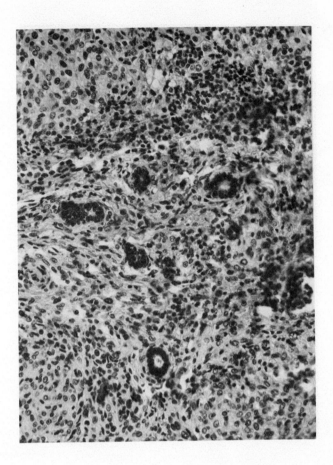

Fig. 127. – Mammary gland tumor, higher magnification of area indicated in Fig. 125. Mammary gland adenofibrosarcoma with small islands of gland formation appearing within the sarcomatous mass. H & E. 250X.

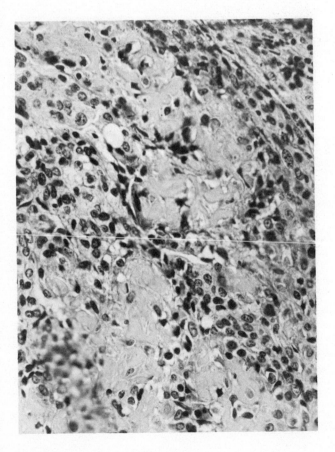

Fig. 128. – Mammary gland adenofibrosarcoma shown in Fig. 125, at higher magnification that in Figs 126 and 127. Deposits of hyalin are seen both intracellularly and extracellularly within the tumor mass. H & E. 400X.

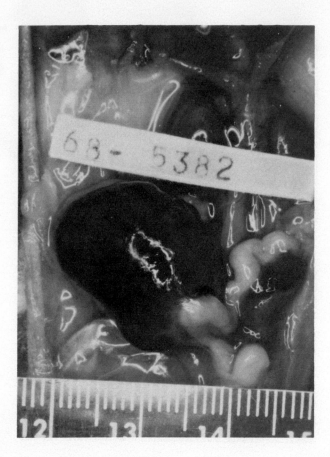

Fig. 129. – Uterine tumor. Large hemorrhagic mass in right horn of the uterus.

Fig. 130. – Hemangioendothelioma of the uterus, microscopic section (130) of tumor seen in Fig. 129 and (131) further magnification of area from section shown in 130. Tumor elements are primarily proliferating endothelial cells, with trapped blood and numerous thrombi. H & E. 25×, 200×.

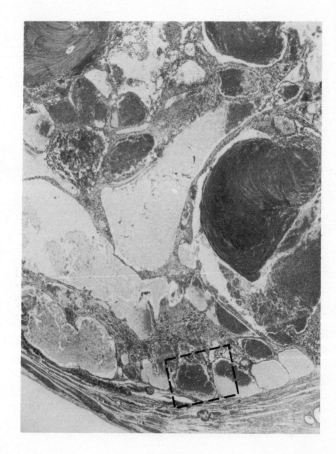

Fig. 131. – Hemangioendothelioma of the uterus, microscopic section (130) of tumor seen in Fig. 129 and (131) further magnification of area from section shown in 130. Tumor elements are primarily proliferating endothelial cells, with trapped blood and numerous thrombi. H & E. 25×, 200×.

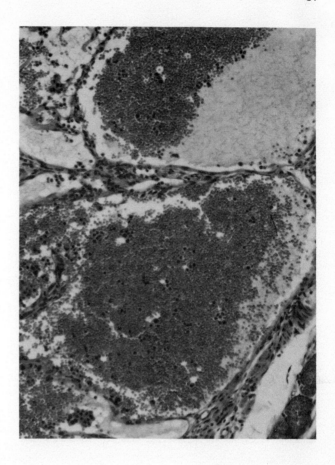

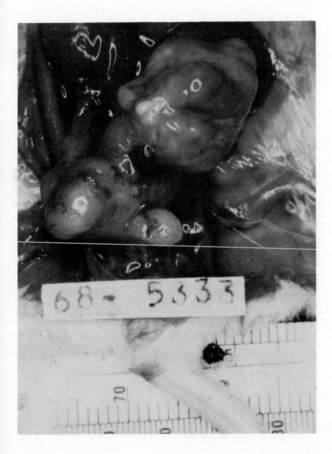

Fig. 132. – Uterine tumor, left horn. Firm mass, 12 × 20 mm.

82

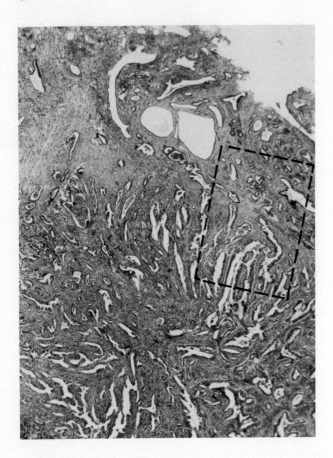

**Fig. 133.** – Uterine tumor, fibroadenocarcinoma. Same tumor as Fig. 132. Bizarre pseudoducts and supportive tissue resulting from the proliferating epithelial cells are seen. H & E. 25×, 95×.

**Fig. 134.** – Uterine tumor, fibroadenocarcinoma. Same tumor as Fig. 132. Bizarre pseudoducts and supportive tissue resulting from the proliferating epithelial cells are seen. H & E. 25×, 95×.

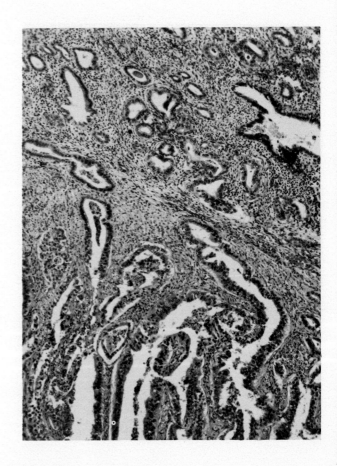

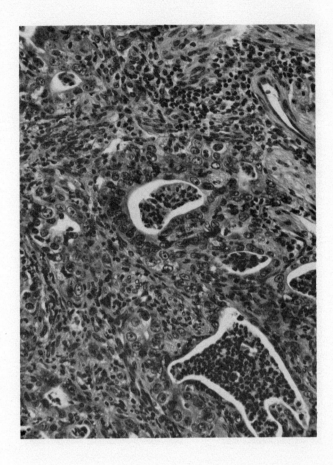

Fig. 135. – Same uterine tumor (fibroadenocarcinoma) as in Figs 132–134, higher magnification. Cells are anaplastic with large nuclear-cytoplasmic ratio, numerous mitotic figures, and cellular atypia. Cellular debris is seen in the pseudoduct structures. H & E. 250×.

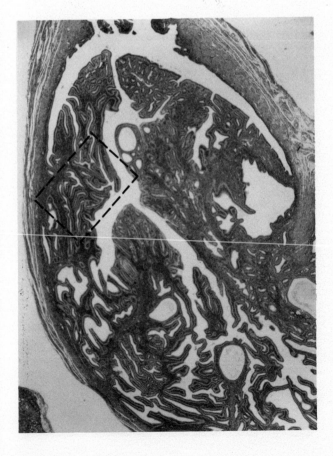

Fig. 136. – Uterine tumor, papillary cystadenoma, benign. The proliferative extension of the mild to severe cystic hyperplasia common in most older animals is shown. H & E. 25×.

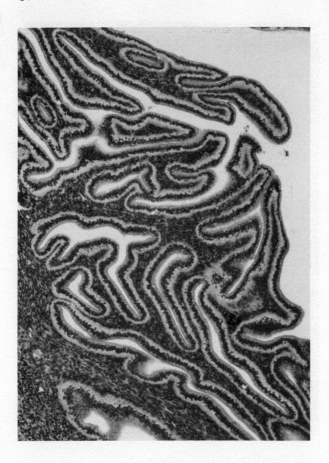

Fig. 137. – Uterine tumor, magnification of area indicated in Fig. 136. Polypoid mass of epithelial cells forms a papillary cystadenoma of the uterus. H & E. 150×.

Fig. 138. – Uterine tumor, cystadenomatous polyp. Mass protrudes into the lumen; dominant cell resembled epithelial cell of uterus. Some tubular structures were evident. H & E. 37×.

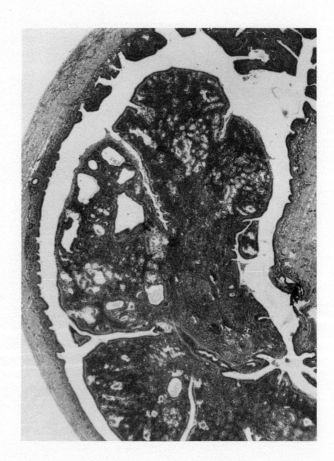

**Fig. 139.** – Section of uterine tumor shown in Fig. 138. Proliferating cells of the polyp are shown. Some tubular structures are necrotic and there is also stromal proliferation. H & E. 200×.

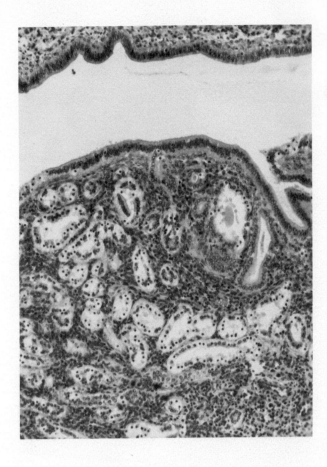

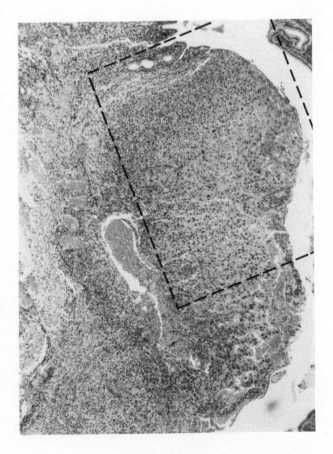

**Fig. 140.** – Uterine tumor. Mass was quite vascular and appeared to be of epithelial origin. Although mice used in the study were virgin, this mass resembled a deciduoma (confirmed by consultant pathologist). H & E. 63×.

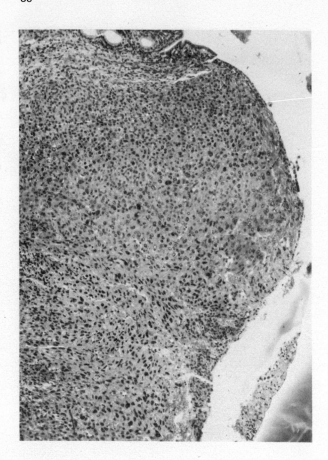

Fig. 141. — Magnification of area of uterine tumor, deciduoma, as indicated on Fig. 140. H & E. 100×.

Fig. 142. — Hepatoma diagnosed at necropsy. Although somewhat larger, with more cytoplasm and pleomorphism, these tumor (H) cells closely resemble hepatic parenchymal cells (P) and form closely packed sheets with some dilation of sinusoids between cells. H & E. 95×.

Fig. 143. – Higher magnification of indicated portion of hepatoma seen in Fig. 142. Tumor (H) was associated with a proliferation of bizarre duct-like structures at the periphery of the tumor and resembled the histological appearance of hepatomas reported in RF mice following diethylnitrosamine (DEN) treatment (19). H & E. 250×.

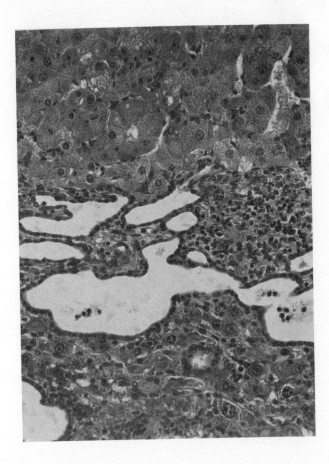

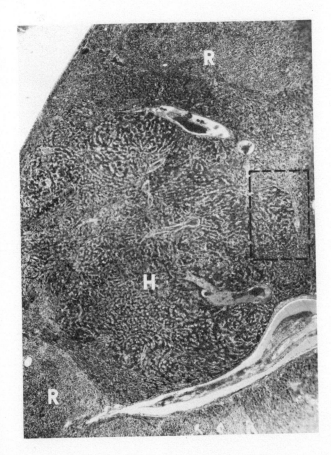

Fig. 144. – Hepatoma (H) concurrent with a reticulum cell sarcoma (R) of the liver. H & E. 25×.

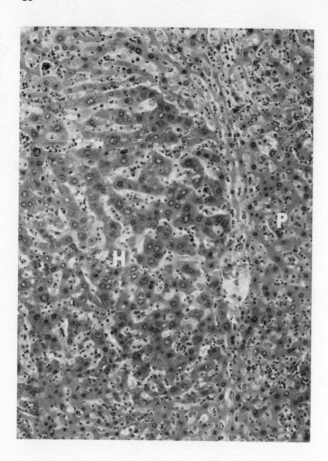

Fig. 145. – Magnified section of hepatoma as indicated on Fig. 144. Margin between hepatoma (H) and nontumorous liver parenchyma (P) is evident. The sinusoids are dilated and the tumor cells are relatively well organized and homogenous in size. H & E. 150×.

Fig. 146. – Further magnification of hepatoma shown in Figs 144 and 145. Tumor cells resemble immature liver cells. The sinusoids are filled with cellular debris, and eosinophilic droplets are seen intracytoplasmically. H & E. 500× (oil).

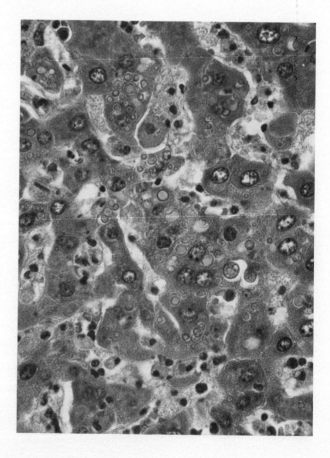

Fig. 147. – Liver tumor (T), accompanying liver abscesses and reticulum cell sarcoma. Auricular thrombosis is also seen.

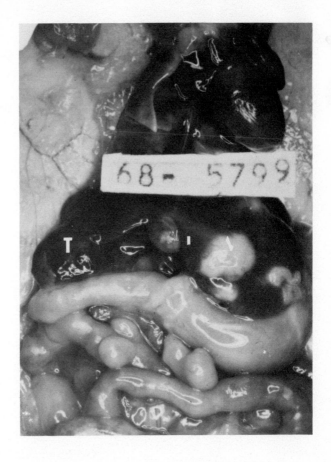

Fig. 148. – Liver tumor, hemangioendothelioma, same tumor as in Fig. 147. A large mass bulges from the liver surface. H & E. 25×.

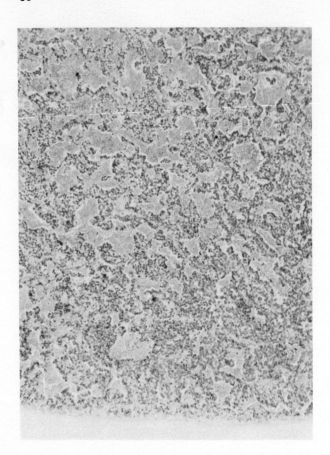

Fig. 149. – Liver tumor, hemangioendothelioma, magnified section as indicated on Fig. 148. Proliferation of endothelial cells with large accumulations of erythrocytes. H & E. 100X.

Fig. 150. – Pheochromocytoma of adrenal medulla, diagnosed histologically. Large cells with abundant cytoplasm which formed cordlike structures are seen. H & E. 50X.

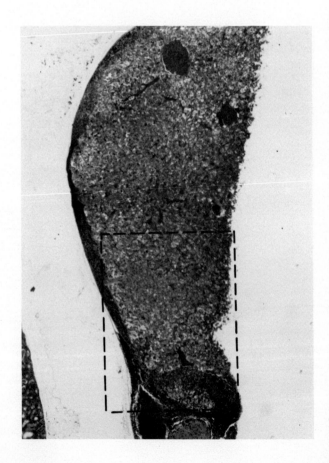

Fig. 151. — Pheochromocytoma of adrenal medulla, magnified section indicated on Fig. 150. Inflammatory cells associated with the tumor process are also seen in the adrenal cortex. Considerable pleomorphism is observed in this tumor. H & E. 100×.

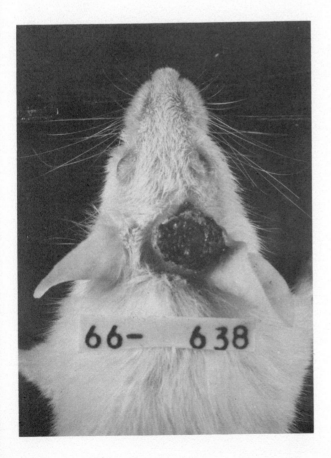

Fig. 152. — Squamous cell carcinoma, right ear. Tumor is ulcerated.

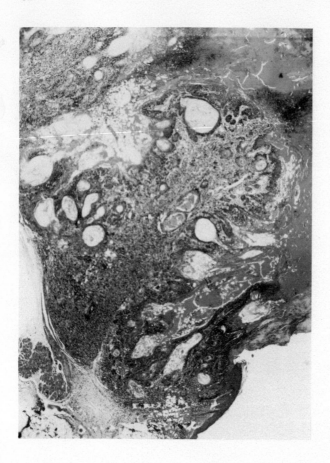

Fig. 153. – Squamous cell carcinoma, right ear, same as Fig. 152. Tumor is very invasive and extends subcutaneously. Numerous areas of mild to severe anaplasia are apparent. H & E. 25×.

Fig. 154. – Squamous cell carcinoma of the ear, higher magnification of Fig. 153. Considerable anaplasia and cellular atypia and numerous mitoses and pleomorphism are seen. H & E. 200×.

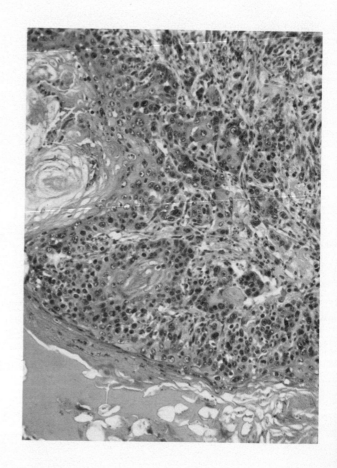

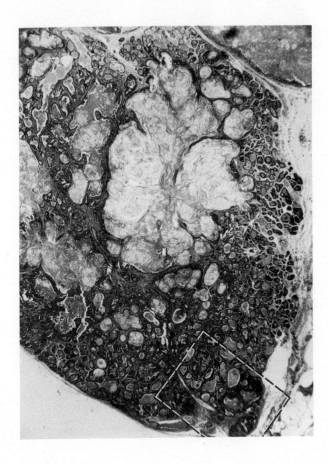

Fig. 155. – Squamous cell carcinoma at the base of the tail. Extensive keratin formation, numerous foci of anaplastic cells, and extensive invasiveness of the tumor are apparent. H & E. 25×.

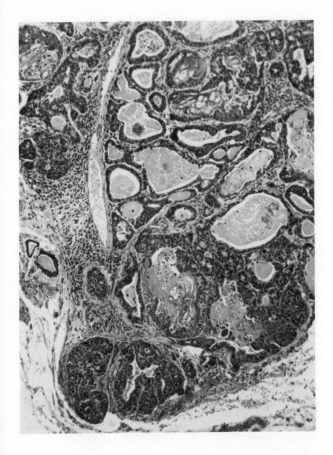

Fig. 156. – Magnified section of the squamous cell carcinoma shown in Fig. 155. There are numerous foci of anaplastic cells, some with keratin formation. The tumor is extensive and invasive. H & E. 100×.

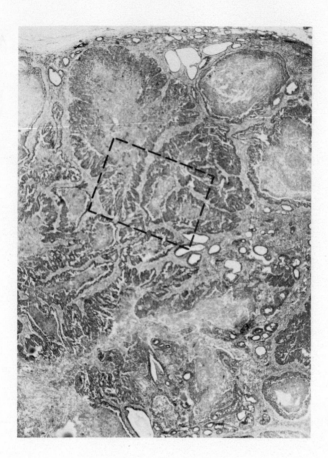

Fig. 157. – Squamous cell carcinoma of the vulva. Tumor was very invasive, and also very anaplastic, with little keratin production. H & E. 25×.

Fig. 158. – Squamous cell carcinoma of the vulva, higher magnification of area indicated on Fig. 157. Very anaplastic tumor is growing rapidly with no keratin formation. H & E. 100×.

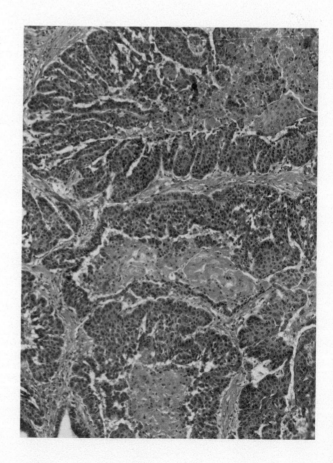

**Fig. 159.** – Harderian gland tumor, unilateral. Right eye is closed and tumor is ulcerating.

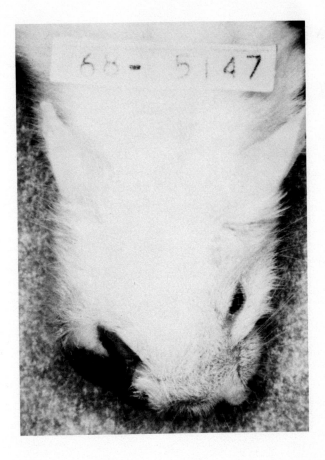

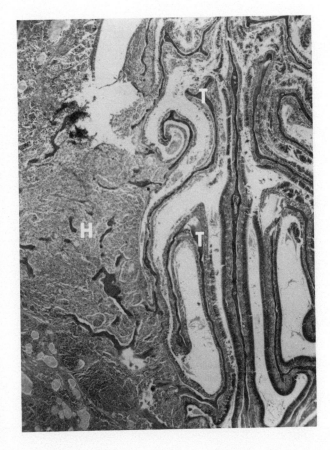

**Fig. 160.** – Microscopic section of Harderian gland tumor shown in Fig. 159. Tumor (H) is exerting pressure on turbinate bones (T). Necrosis of epithelial lining and of turbinates is evident. H & E. 25×.

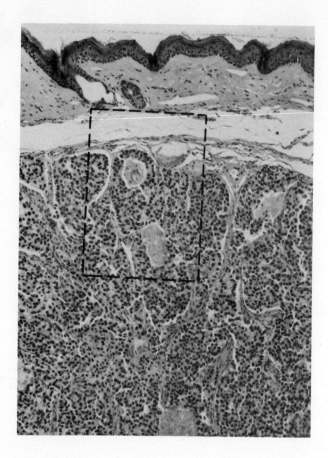

**Fig. 161.** – Harderian gland tumor, higher magnification of Fig. 159. Tumor cells formed glandlike structures. H & E. 150×.

**Fig. 162.** – Harderian gland adenocarcinoma, higher magnification of area indicated on Fig. 161. Cells are hyperchromatic with moderate cytoplasm. Glandlike structures are evident and tumor is invasive. H & E. 375×.

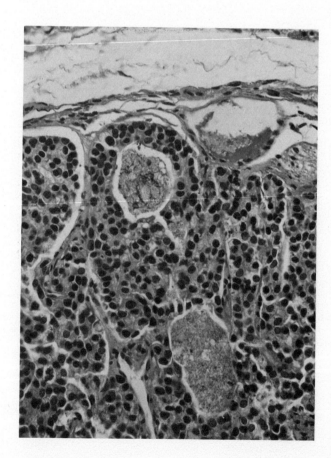

Fig. 163. – Harderian gland adenoma, more differentiated than Figs 159–162. Tumor diagnosed at necropsy. Normal Harderian gland tissue (H) is evident. Tumor is not invasive. H & E. 25×.

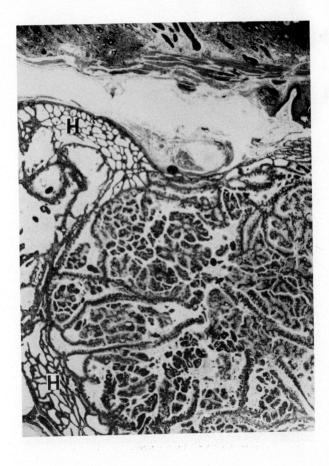

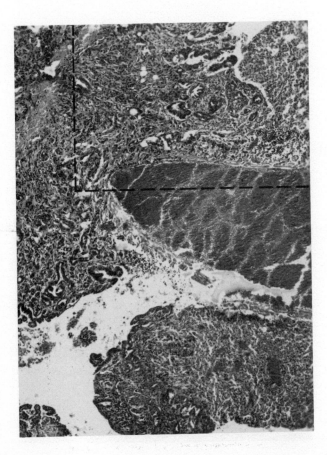

Fig. 164. – Anaplastic adenocarcinoma of the lung. While primary malignant neoplasm in the lung of the RF mouse is rare, this tumor was considered to be primary in the lung. Cells were very anaplastic, formed pseudoducts, and had considerable pleomorphic structure. H & E. 63×.

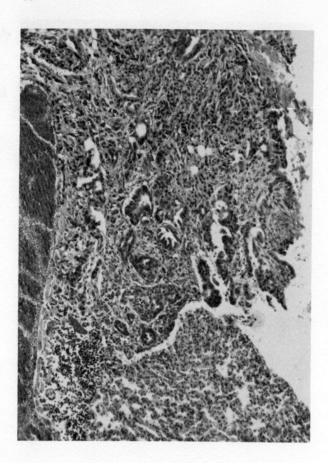

Fig. 165. – Primary adenocarcinoma of the lung, same as Fig. 164. Ductlike structures and stromal tissues are proliferating with considerable anaplasia. H & E. 100×.

Fig. 166. – Adenocarcinoma (CA), metastatic in the mediastinal lymph nodes (LN). Same animal as in Figs 164 and 165. Cellular morphology is the same as in the primary lesion. H&E. 100×.

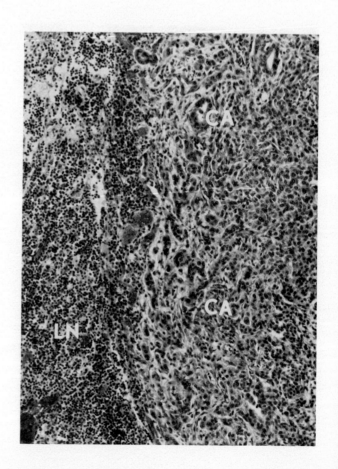

Fig. 167. – Metastatic foci (CA) in the left ventricle of the heart. Same animal as in Figs 164–166. Adenocarcinoma was primary in the lung. H & E. 25×.

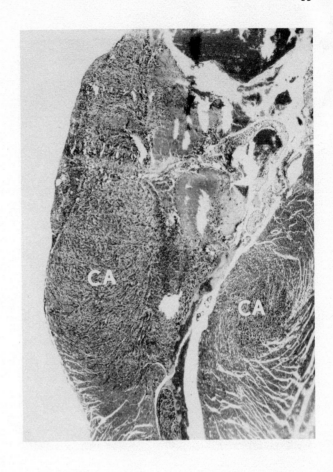

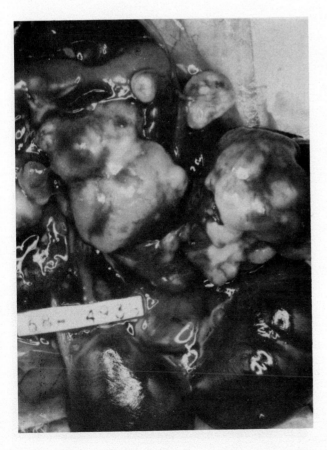

Fig. 168. – Multiple tumor of undetermined origin in the abdomen. Kidney was suspected as the primary organ site with abdominal metastases. Animal also had a reticulum cell sarcoma.

100

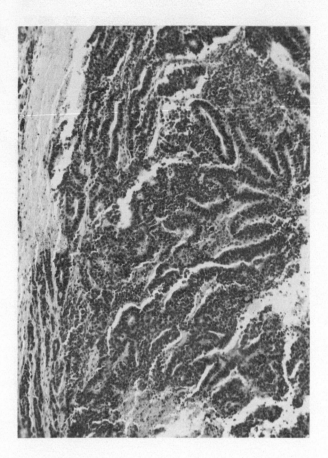

Fig. 169. – Moderately differentiated adenocarcinoma, same as Fig. 168. Tubular adenocarcinoma possibly was primary in the kidney. The tumor cells are very invasive and pleomorphism is seen. H & E. 100×.

Fig. 170. – Abdominal tumor. Large mass extended into the inguinal area, but appeared to be primary in the abdomen rather than in the mammary gland tissue.

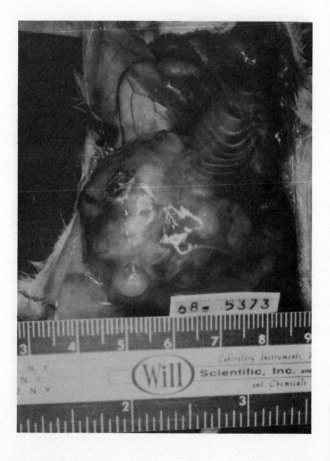

Fig. 171. — Abdominal tumor with abdomen reflected, same as in Fig. 170. Mass is cystic and polypoid and appears to involve primarily the peritoneum.

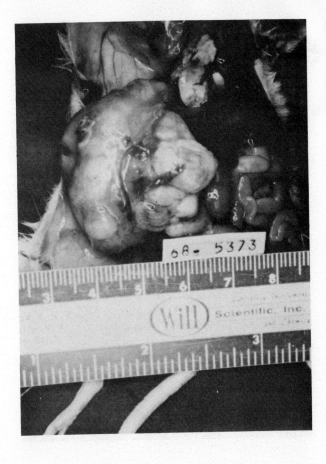

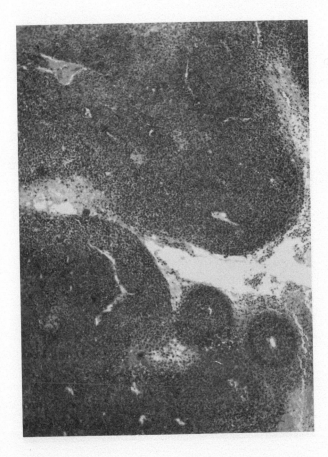

Fig. 172. — Abdominal tumor. Microscopic section of same tumor as shown in Figs 170 and 171. Tumor cells tended to be nodular, concentric, and perivascular. Center of mass was necrotic; mass was more or less homogeneous. H & E. 95X.

102

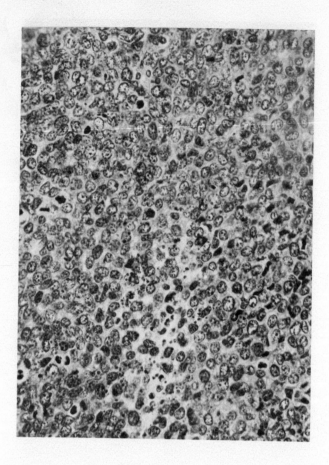

Fig. 173. — Same tumor cells as in Fig. 172 at higher magnification. Cells are hypochromatic, with a high nuclear-cytoplasmic ratio, prominent nucleoli, high mitotic index, and epithelial-like appearance. Cellular necrosis was evident in rapidly growing areas. Tumor was diagnosed as a mesothelioma originating from peritoneum (consultant pathologist confirmed this impression). H & E. 370X.

Fig. 174. — Auricular thrombosis. Auricle markedly distended by light colored mass.

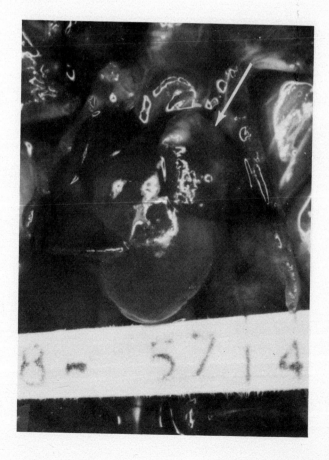

Fig. 175. – Auricular thrombosis, with near total occlusion. H & E. 25×.

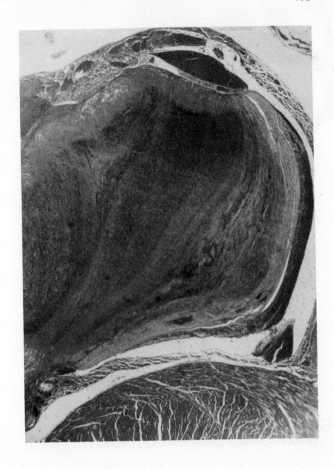

Fig. 176. – Auricular thrombosis, with partial occlusion, same as Fig. 174. H & E. 25×.

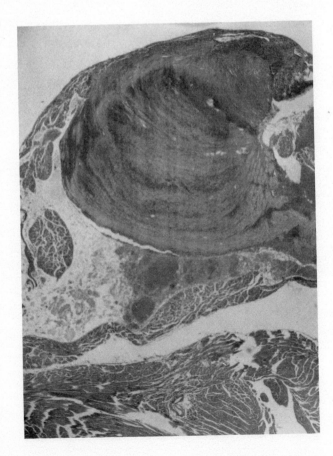

104

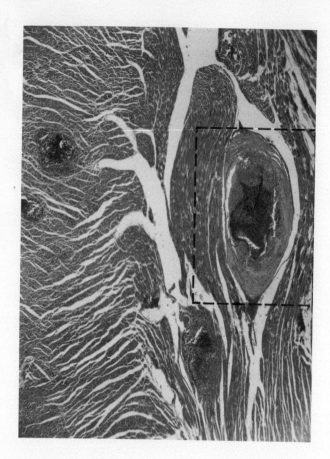

Fig. 177. – Ventricular mural thrombosis, left ventricle, usually detected histologically. Microabscesses are also seen in the myocardium. H & E. 25×.

Fig. 178. – Ventricular thrombosis, higher magnification of section indicated on Fig. 177. Thrombus attached to left ventricular wall. H & E. 63×.

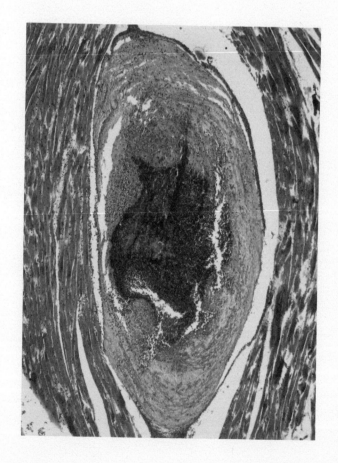

**Fig. 179.** – Generalized polyarteritis of aorta and branching arteries. Thoracic and abdominal aorta are included. Aneurysms are seen.

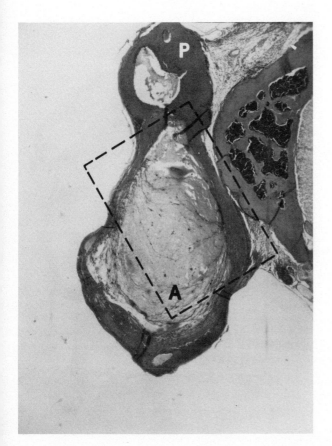

**Fig. 180.** – Polyarteritis (P) and aneurysm (A) of aorta, same as in Fig. 179. Aneurysm contains thrombus. H & E. 25×.

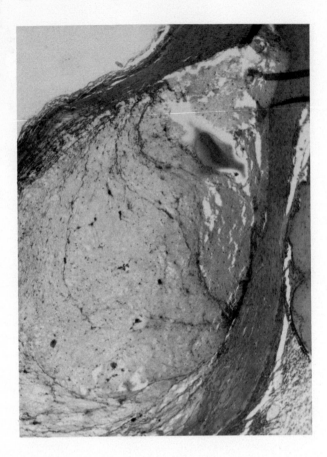

Fig. 181. – Polyarteritis of the aorta and aneurysmal dilatation, magnification of section indicated on Fig. 180. Fibrin of thrombus is also seen. H & E. 63×.

Fig. 182. – Polyarteritis of aorta and branching arteries. Inflammatory process is seen in the perivascular areas. Thickening of the arterial wall and clotting process are also evident. Vertebra (V); spinal cord (S). H & E. 25×.

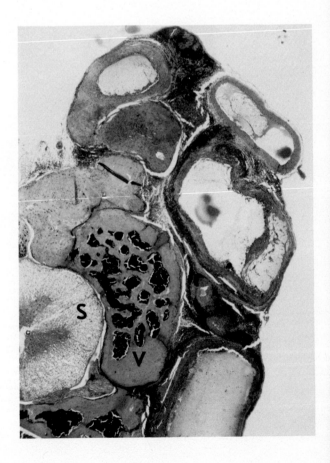

Fig. 183. – Polyarteritis of aorta (A) and branching arteries (B), same mouse as in Figs 179–182. Proliferative changes are seen in media, adventitia, and periarterial tissue, with partial occlusion by a mural thrombus in one artery. Inflammatory cells appear in the perivascular area. H & E. 63×.

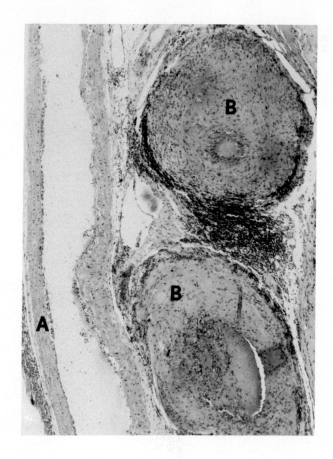

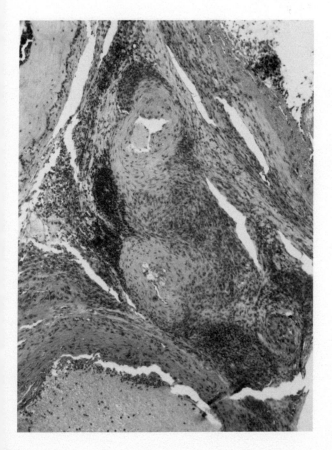

Fig. 184. – Polyarteritis of smaller vessels, higher magnification of Fig. 182. Walls of the small arterioles are markedly thickened; inflammatory cells appear predominantly in the outer layers and perivascular tissue of the arterioles. H & E. 100×.

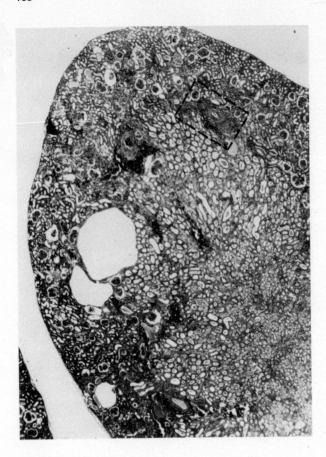

Fig. 185. – Polyarteritis, kidney, same mouse as in Figs 204–209. Cystic areas are seen in cortex. H & E. 25×.

Fig. 186. – Polyarteritis of arterioles, higher magnification of area indicated on Fig. 185. One vessel was occluded with proliferative changes. Glomerulosclerosis: moderate. H & E. 200×.

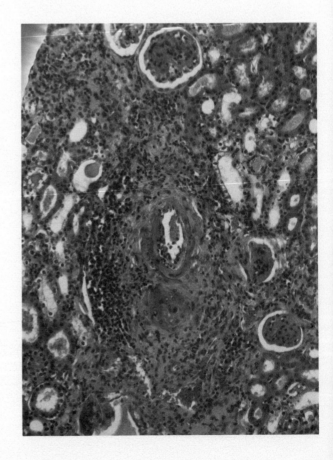

Fig. 187. – Polyarteritis involving the coronary vessels, a very common site for this disease. Necrosis of adventitia, perivascular tissue, and surrounding muscle tissue. Proliferation is usually not as extensive in media of coronary vessels as in peripheral arteries and arterioles. H & E. 100×.

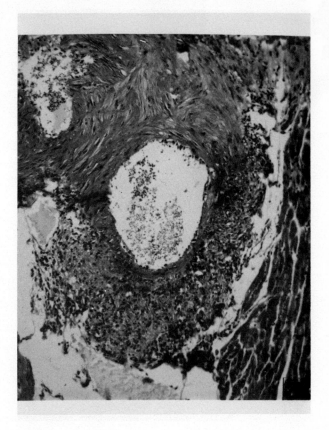

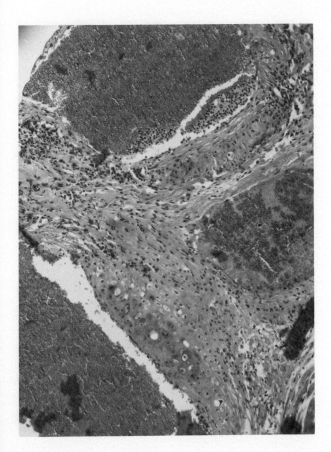

Fig. 188. – Polyarteritis, coronary vessels. Inflammatory cells infiltrated with necrosis. Chondrification accompanied polyarteritis. H & E. 100×.

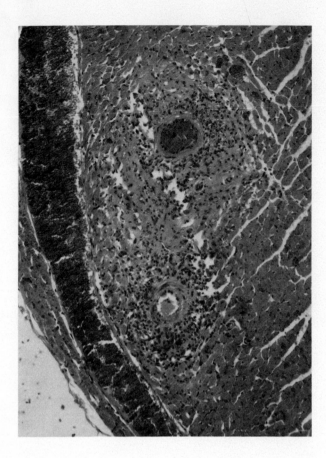

Fig. 189. – Polyarteritis, coronary vessels. Smaller coronary arterioles are infiltrated perivascularly by chronic inflammatory cells and there is muscle necrosis. H & E. 160×.

Fig. 190. – Polyarteritis, coronary vessels. Infiltration of inflammatory cells is seen. Proliferation of the media is present in the smaller arterioles. H & E. 300×.

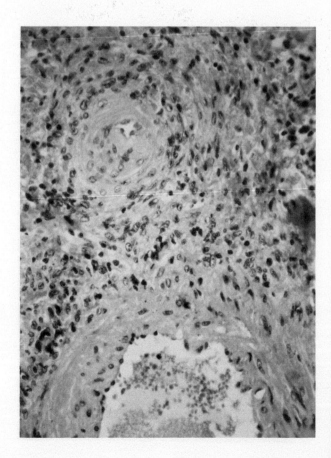

Fig. 191. – Polyarteritis and arterial hyalinization, adrenal gland. Involvement of several arterioles of the adrenal cortex is extensive and there is concurrent deposition of hyalin-like material immediately beneath the endothelial surface of the arterioles. H & E. 150×.

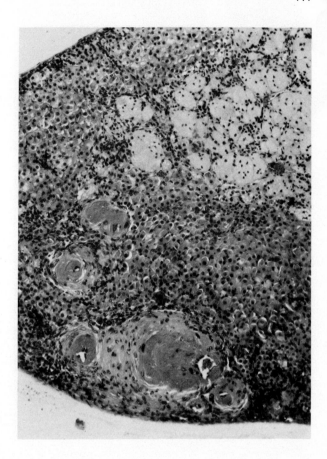

Fig. 192. – Polyarteritis, spleen. Splenic arteries and arterioles are involved. H & E. 100×.

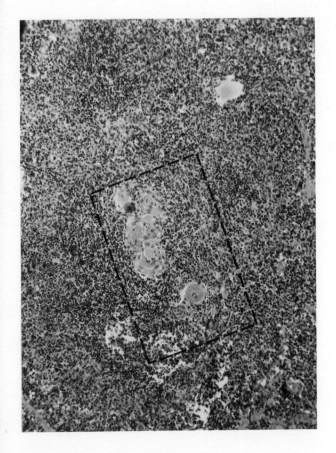

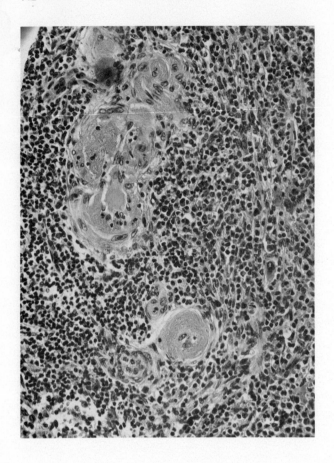

**Fig. 193.** – Polyarteritis, splenic arterioles, higher magnification of area indicated on Fig. 192. Perivascular proliferative and inflammatory response with hyalin deposition beneath the surface of endothelium is shown. H & E. 250×.

**Fig. 194.** – Polyarteritis, phlebitis, of femoral artery and vein. H & E. 25×.

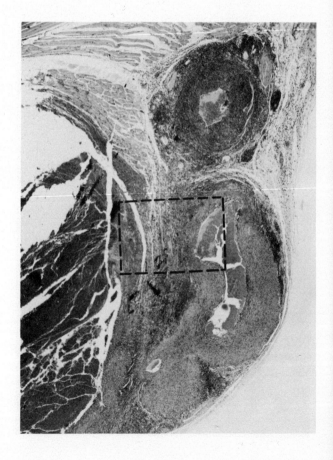

Fig. 195. – Polyarteritis in femoral artery (A) and inflammatory response involving vein (V), higher magnification of area indicated on Fig. 194. A fibrinous clot is forming. H & E. 100×.

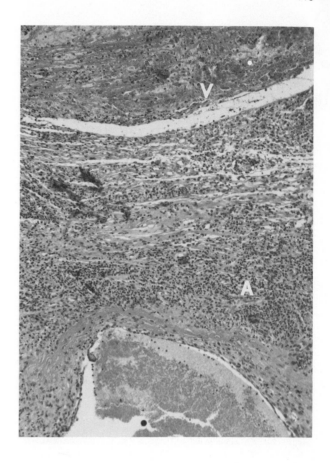

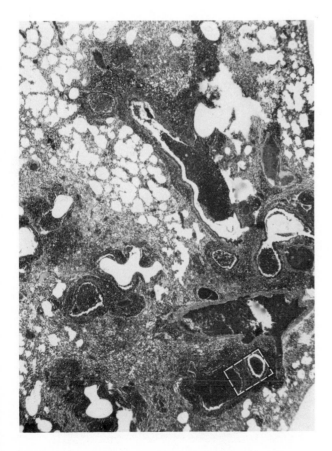

Fig. 196. – Acute bronchopneumonia. Infiltrative inflammatory cells are located in the bronchi, bronchioles, and smaller air passages, both peribronchially and perivascularly. H & E. 25×.

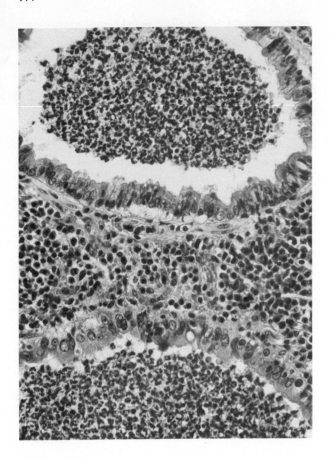

Fig. 197. – Acute bronchopneumonia. Magnification of area marked on Fig. 196. Pus is seen in the bronchioles, and inflammatory cells are observed in peribronchial area. H & E. 375×.

Fig. 198. – Abscess, myocardium, often multiple; most often diagnosed histologically. Necrosis of myocardial fibers and infiltration of other inflammatory cells are evident. H & E. 150×.

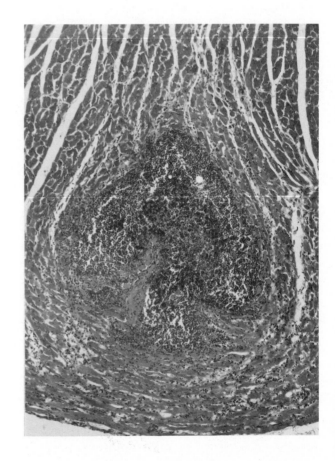

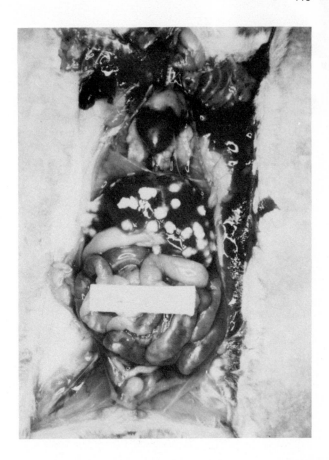

Fig. 199. – Multiple liver abscesses and pulmonary tumors. Abscesses are of cheesy consistency, white, and have irregular, rough surfaces.

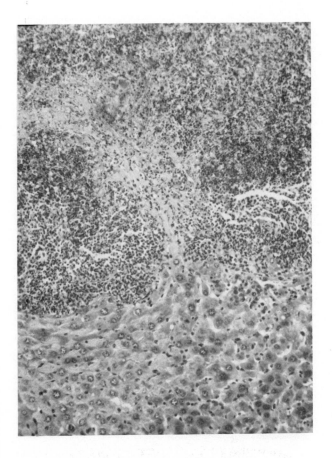

Fig. 200. – Liver abscesses. Microscopic section from liver in Fig. 199. Pressure necrosis on liver parenchyma, with displacement of parenchyma, is evident. H & E. 200×.

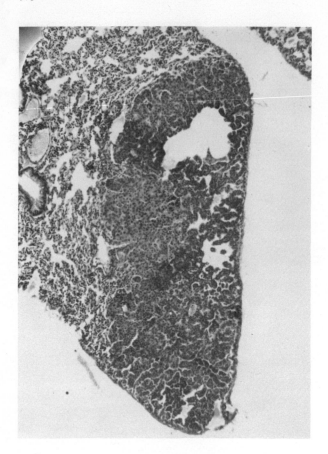

Fig. 201. – Lung tumor, same as Fig. 199. Papillary adenoma is primary in lung. H & E. 95×.

Fig. 202. – Glomerulosclerosis, severe. Deposition of homogeneous eosinophilic material within capillary loops of the glomeruli is shown and numerous intratubular casts are seen. Functional ability of the kidney is questionable. H & E. 100×.

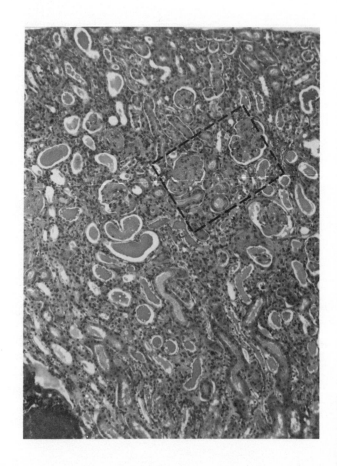

Fig. 203. – Glomerulosclerosis, severe, magnification of area indicated in Fig. 202. Deposition of hyalin material within the capillary loops is apparent. Casts are seen intratubularly. Function of the glomeruli is certainly inhibited. H & E. 400×.

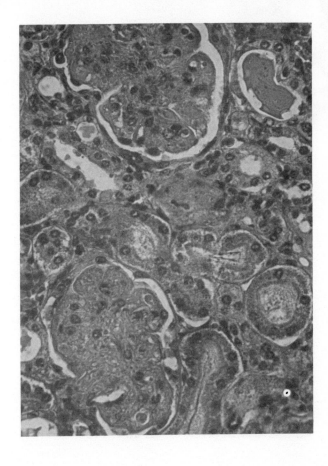

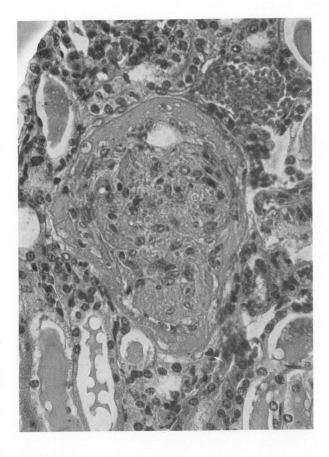

Fig. 204. – Glomerulosclerosis, severe, same as Fig. 202. An unusual pattern of deposition outside the capillary loops and within Bowman's capsule is shown. H & E. 400×.

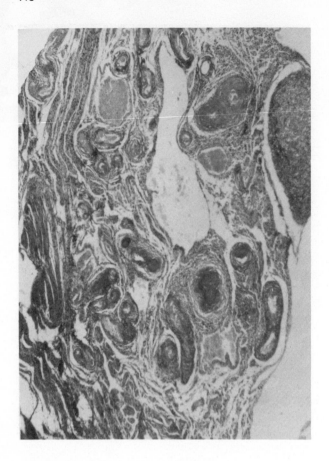

Fig. 205. – Hyalin deposition, arteriole of uterus. Material is eosinophilic and amorphous and is deposited just beneath the endothelial lining. H & E. 63×.

Fig. 206. – Hyalin deposition in spermatic artery of RF male. Material is homogeneous and shows no inflammatory response within the artery. Hyalinization can occur in conjunction with polyarteritis or may occur without any obvious inflammatory process. H & E. 400×.

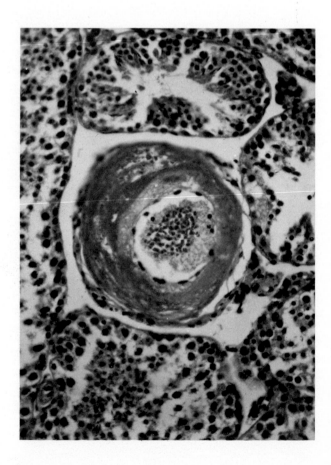

**Fig. 207.** – Chondrification at valvular attachment, heart. Inflammatory cells (myocarditis) surround the area of cartilage formation. H & E. 150×.

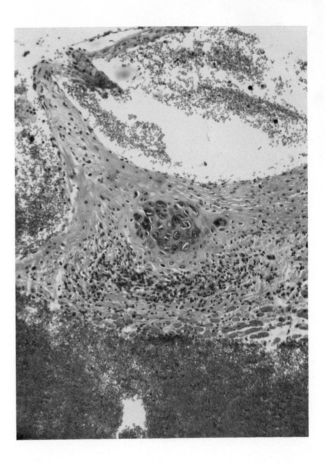

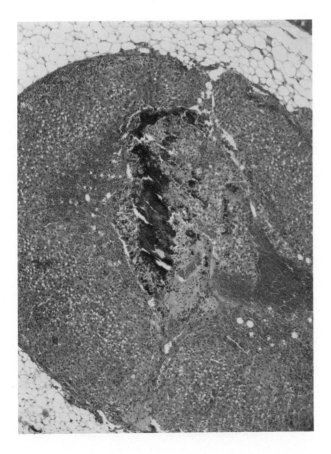

**Fig. 208.** – Calcification, adrenal medulla, associated with prior hemorrhage of long standing. H & E. 63×.

Fig. 209. – Ectopic ossification of spleen; obliteration of entire splenic architecture. H & E. 25×.

Fig. 210. – Ectopic ossification throughout spleen, higher magnification of Fig. 209. Etiology was considered metabolic rather than malignant. H & E. 150×.

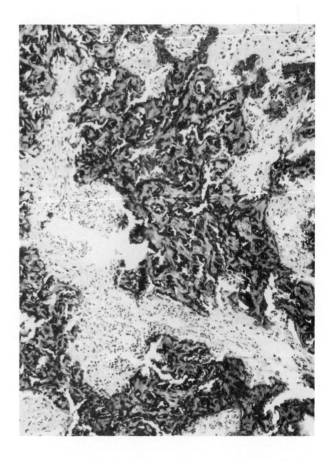

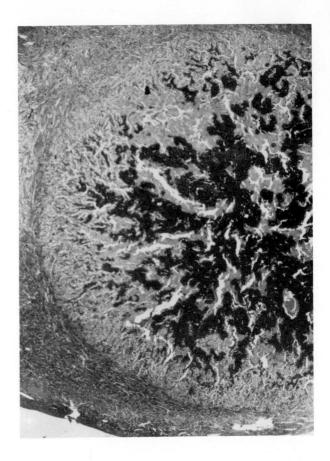

Fig. 211. – Ectopic ossification, metastatic to ovary in the same mouse as in Fig. 209. Ovarian tumor is in the periphery and around focus of ossification. H&E. 25×.

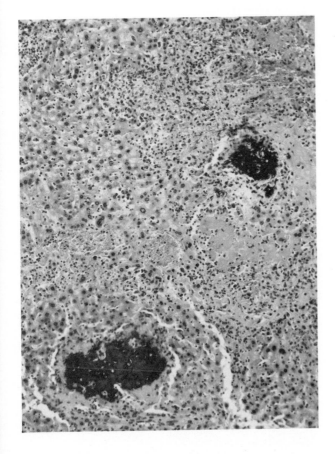

Fig. 212. – Ectopic ossification, metastatic to liver in the same mouse as in Fig. 209. Foci of necrosis and inflammatory cells surround the ossifying foci. H & E. 100×.

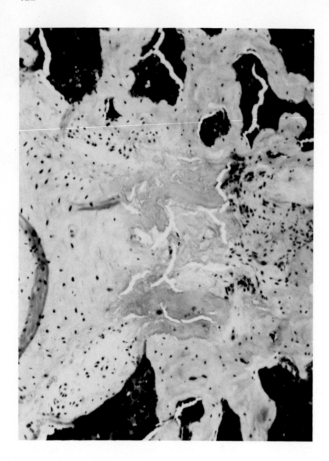

Fig. 213. — Sternal necrosis. Necrosis appears in the intersternebral region with acellularity and an amorphous eosinophilic deposit. H & E. 150×.

Fig. 214. — Sternal necrosis. Amorphous eosinophilic necrosis is seen in areas of endochondral ossification and chondrification of the sternebral bodies. H & E. 100×.

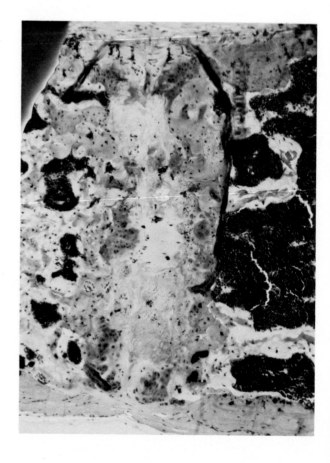

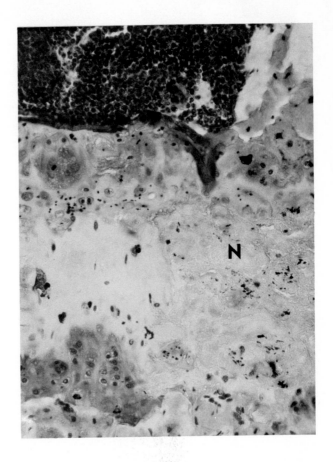

Fig. 215. — Sternal necrosis, higher magnification of Fig. 214. Foci are visible where necrosis is taking place (N). H & E. 250×.

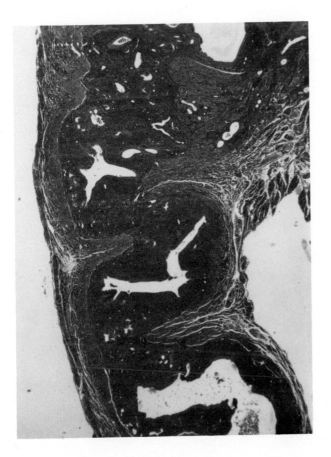

Fig. 216. — Uterine hyperplasia, characteristic of all aging female mice. Hyperplasia of the uterine mucosa and supportive tissue with accompanying microcysts is shown. H & E. 37×.

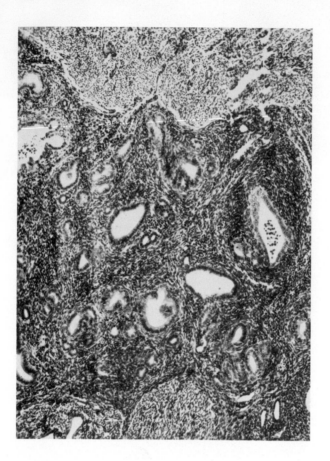

Fig. 217. — Uterine hyperplasia, as in Fig. 216. Proliferation of the uterine mucosa and supportive tissue, and microcyst formation are seen. H & E. 100×.

Fig. 218. — Calculi, occasionally found in urinary bladder. Associated thickening of the epithelial wall with granulomatous inflammation is apparent. H & E. 25×.

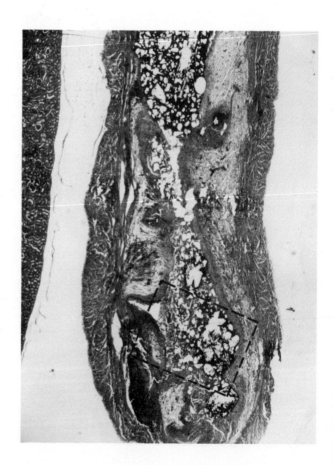

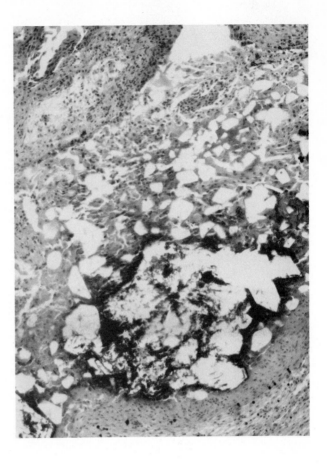

Fig. 219. – Cystic calculi with granulomatous inflammation of urinary bladder, magnification of area indicated on Fig. 218. H & E. 100×.

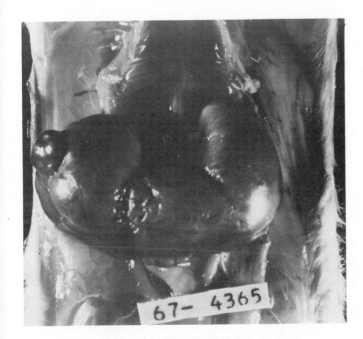

Fig. 220. – Anomaly of left kidney. Aplasia of the kidney cortex with distension is evident and cavity is fluid-filled. Only a thin layer of cortical cells remain. Condition was considered congenital.

7188